ANGLO-SAXON
VERNACULAR MANUSCRIPTS
IN AMERICA

EXHIBITED AT
THE PIERPONT MORGAN LIBRARY
1 APRIL – 9 MAY
1976

Anglo-Saxon

Vernacular Manuscripts

in America

Rowland L. Collins

The Scheide Library

The Pierpont Morgan Library

NEW YORK · 1976

CONTENTS

 PREFACE

IT SEEMS especially appropriate that The Pierpont Morgan Library and The Scheide Library should jointly present this exhibition of Anglo-Saxon Vernacular Manuscripts in America since the two libraries have had close and beneficial relations for many years. Both libraries have grown from collections begun by young men in their school days in the mid-nineteenth century and both libraries have extraordinary examples of early books and manuscripts such as the manuscripts in this exhibition.

We take great pleasure in sponsoring this gathering of all the known Old English manuscripts in America, assembled under the supervision of Rowland L. Collins, Chairman of the Department of English, The University of Rochester, who has also prepared the catalogue for the exhibition. Professor Collins has acknowledged the generous cooperation of the institutions and their staffs who have made this occasion possible. We wish to express our special thanks to him and to all of the other scholars and the institutions they represent.

We are most grateful to Mr. Roderick D. Stinehour and his associates at The Stinehour Press, and also to our friends at The Meriden Gravure Company, for their distinguished work in the design and printing of this volume.

CHARLES RYSKAMP
WILLIAM H. SCHEIDE

ACKNOWLEDGMENTS

SCHOLARS everywhere are indebted to the present owners of manuscripts which contain Anglo-Saxon. They have preserved, whether through chance or careful planning, whether through windfall or financial sacrifice, the priceless treasures of our past. I am grateful to Mr. William Scheide, to The Pierpont Morgan Library, to Mr. James M. Osborn, to the Beinecke Library of Yale University, to the Free Library of Philadelphia, to The Lilly Library of Indiana University, and to the Library of the University of Kansas, not only for making their holdings available to me over the past years but for their willingness to share their manuscripts for the exhibit which occasioned this catalogue. In addition, the staffs of The British Library, The Bodleian Library, and the Libraries of Corpus Christi College and Queens' College, Cambridge, have given me access to closely related manuscripts and fragments in British libraries.

Many individuals have given me special assistance. The late David Randall encouraged my initial interest in the Lilly Library fragments. Miss Alexandra Mason, Miss Jean Preston, Professor Louis L. Martz, Miss Marjorie Wynne, Professor Peter Clemoes (especially in our collaboration on studies of what is here called MS 3), Mr. Howell J. Heaney, Mr. Herman W. Liebert, Mrs. William Scheide, Mr. Michael Morton-Smith, Dr. John H. Plummer, Professor John C. Pope, Mr. William M. Voelkle, and Dr. Charles Ryskamp have each helped me in important ways. The Indiana University Foundation and the College of Arts and Science at the University of Rochester have generously assisted my travel in search of manuscript fragments.

Nothing of merit can ever be written on Old English manuscripts without great debt to Dr. Neil R. Ker. His monumental *Catalogue*

9

(Oxford, 1957) stands as the source of full and accurate information to which all subsequent work has provided but modest addenda.

I am grateful to my wife for help with the text, and to my wife and children for tolerating my absences from home with good grace and for failing to complain significantly about my irritability when I discovered one more error in my own notes. And I am grateful to Mrs. Helen Craven and to Mrs. Sheila Robertson for the careful typing of the manuscript. My greatest debt of all, however, is to Mr. William Scheide, for his generosity over the years and for allowing his library to be the headquarters of my work, and to Mrs. Mina Ruese Bryan, the librarian of The Scheide Library. She has encouraged this work and has served as my first reader and editor. She has, further, insured that each step was pleasant and worthwhile.

All errors, and there are bound to be some, are my own fault.

R.L.C.

LIST OF ILLUSTRATIONS

PLATE 1

MS 1a: Yale University, MS 401, fol. 7r; glosses to Aldhelm

PLATE 2

MS 1b: Free Library of Philadelphia, J. F. Lewis MS ET 121, recto;
glosses to Aldhelm

PLATE 3

MS 2: Yale University, MS 578, verso; *St. Mark* 1:39–42

PLATE 4

MSS 3a and b: Osborn Collection, two strips, recto; Ælfric, *Catholic Homilies I,
Homily for Palm Sunday*, and: Indiana University, MS Poole 10, recto;
Ælfric, *Lives of Saints, Lives of St. Apollonaris and Kings Abdon and Sennes*

MS 4: Indiana University, MS Add. 1000, recto; Ælfric, *Grammar*

PLATE 5

MS 5: University of Kansas, Pryce MS P2A:1, recto; glossary

PLATE 6

MS 6: University of Kansas, Pryce MS C2:1, verso;
The Legend of the Cross

PLATE 7

MS 7: University of Kansas, Pryce MS C2:2, verso;
Ælfric, *De uno confessore*

PLATES 8 AND 9

MS 8: The Scheide Library, MS 71, fols. 126v and 127r;
The Blickling Homilies, the analogue to Grendel's mere in *Beowulf*

12

INTRODUCTION

ANY MANUSCRIPT which preserves so much as a phrase of original Anglo-Saxon is a notable relic. In 1957, Dr. Neil R. Ker published his monumental *Catalogue of Manuscripts Containing Anglo-Saxon* and he was able to describe only a little over four hundred such manuscripts ("except cartularies and single-sheet documents") still extant today. Since that time a few additional fragments have been discovered; but, barring a miracle, our knowledge of English before 1200 will be limited to the group of manuscripts described by Ker. The English language before the Norman Conquest is called both Old English (by those who see it primarily as the precursor of Middle English—the language of Chaucer—and Modern English) and Anglo-Saxon (by those who stress the continental Germanic roots of English society). Old English or Anglo-Saxon is the English spoken before the great influence of French following the Norman invasions of 1066. Although our enormous Modern English vocabulary reflects the ability of English to absorb words from almost all other languages, the basic structure of the language we speak today was determined by Anglo-Saxon, a language for which written records are rare and precious.

There are three great collections of manuscripts of Anglo-Saxon texts, all in England: The British Library, The Bodleian Library at Oxford, and the Library of Corpus Christi College, Cambridge. The collection of Sir Robert Cotton (1571–1631), in spite of a disastrous fire in 1731, formed the great core of the superb collection in The British Library. Many donors, including Cotton, contributed to building the splendid collection at Oxford, but the collections of Hatton, Junius, and Archbishop Laud were particularly important.

13

The collection at Corpus Christi College is largely the result of the efforts of one man, Matthew Parker, Archbishop of Canterbury from 1559 to 1575. Parker has been called a plunderer of the ancient monastic libraries, but our debt to his acquisitiveness and care for his treasures is strong and clear.

There are manuscripts containing Anglo-Saxon in many other European libraries, from Dublin to Dresden, from Copenhagen to Vercelli. Until this century, however, there was not one original Anglo-Saxon manuscript known to be in America. But in the past six decades, libraries have gradually acquired a remarkable, if small, group of vernacular manuscripts from this period. There are now thirteen of these manuscripts in the United States—here discussed together for the first time—which represent a variety of literary genres, manifest considerable palaeographical interest, and demonstrate with frightful clarity the perilous history of manuscripts containing Anglo-Saxon.

Although Americans rebelled against English rule, they have long been fascinated with the Anglo-Saxon origins of their language. Thomas Jefferson himself, in his plan for the University of Virginia, emphasized that "the pure Anglo-Saxon constitutes at this day the basis of our language" and set up its study as a standard part of the curriculum. The formal study of Anglo-Saxon did not take its place as a standard course quite so rapidly as Jefferson wished. Only in the nineteenth century, when English competed with classical languages for a place in the academic sun, did Anglo-Saxon find a niche in the regular course of English Studies—and then, ironically, often only to prove that English was as difficult as Latin or Greek and, "therefore," as worthy of careful study.

The very first original manuscripts of Anglo-Saxon to reach America seem, ironically, to have been lost. In 1912, Mr. Coella Lindsay Ricketts, the owner of The Scriptorium in Chicago, purchased a number of fragments from the British dealer Tregaskis. When De-Ricci took his original *Census* he saw in Chicago two "Anglo-Saxon MSS. Fragments of two 9th century MSS. on vellum." One was apparently part of a legal treatise; the other, part of a saint's life. De-

Ricci specifically observed "34 lines on two folio half-leaves, both sides being intact and in good state." When The Lilly Library purchased the entire Ricketts Collection in the early nineteen-sixties, these fragments were nowhere to be found. And sadly, Mr. Ricketts's heirs have no memory of where they may be.

As far as is now apparent, the first words of Anglo-Saxon in original manuscript which we still have came to America in 1914. John F. Lewis of Philadelphia that year purchased a leaf from a ninth-century manuscript of Aldhelm's *De laudibus virginitatis* on which seven of the original Latin words were glossed in Anglo-Saxon, probably of the late tenth century (MS 1b).

Mr. Lewis's opportunity was unusual, for American libraries were not able to acquire resources in this field very rapidly; an exceptional chance came in 1932, however, when the Marquess of Lothian sold some thirty-five manuscripts from his library at Blickling Hall. The manuscripts came to New York for sale on 27 January. Lothian lot no. 1, the great eighth-century Psalter of the Roman version, now known as the Blickling Psalter, was purchased by Rosenbach and sold at cost to The Pierpont Morgan Library on 3 February 1932; words on many pages were glossed in Anglo-Saxon of the tenth century and a few vernacular glosses seem to be one or two centuries earlier (MS 10). That same evening, the single most important Anglo-Saxon codex still in private hands, the Blickling Homilies (Lothian lot no. 2), was sold to Barnet J. Beyer (MS 8). This magnificent book of eighteen tenth-century vernacular sermons had been published in the nineteenth century by the Early English Text Society and was widely recognized as the only manuscript of its kind which would ever be sold on the open market. But the sale to Beyer turned out to be a rigged protection of the price. In order to make the auction house as good as its reputation, this unusual manuscript was absorbed into the collection of the owner of the house, Cortlandt Field Bishop. Mr. Bishop died three years later and when his books were sold in 1938 Mr. John Hinsdale Scheide, of Titusville, Pennsylvania, won the prize. Mr. Scheide was particularly pleased to have this book which he saw as a vital vernacular link between his great collection of Bibles and his extraordinary collections of Americana. It was a unique part of the linguistic and religious heritage of American civilization.

The next piece of original Anglo-Saxon came to America in 1947. Mr. George A. Poole, Jr., of Chicago, bought two strips (about half one original leaf) of Ælfric's *Lives of Saints* through Messrs. Robinson of Pall Mall; these fragmentary Anglo-Saxon texts were valued examples for Mr. Poole's growing collection of illustrations for the development of printing styles (MS 3b). In 1954, Mr. Frank Glenn of Kansas City bought a single leaf of the Harleian glossary and sold it that same year to the University of Kansas (MS 5). Within three years, the University of Kansas unwittingly tripled its stock of rare Anglo-Saxon fragments. In 1957 the University Library purchased, at Pearson's in Cambridge, a copy of the second edition of the Kingsmill Long translation of Barclay's *Argenis* (London, 1636). I note "unwittingly," for it was not until 1961 or so that two leaves of Anglo-Saxon narrative were found in the padding for the binding of this book. The first was a part of *The Legend of the Cross* (MS 6); and the second, part of an Ælfrician homily (MS 7).

The late fifties were especially important years for the arrival of Anglo-Saxon fragments in America. In 1957, or shortly before, the New York dealer H.P. Kraus acquired a number of items from the collection of Wilfred Merton, London. Seven of these were offered for sale in 1958 and one of the items was a bifolium of Aldhelm's *De laudibus virginitatis* (related to the Lewis fragment, by this time at the Free Library of Philadelphia) with seventeen interlinear glosses in Anglo-Saxon. These conjugate leaves did not sell rapidly, for Kraus offered them again in 1961 and they are reported to have been sold some time after that to a private collector in Europe. In the same Kraus catalogue (1961) were also offered four leaves of Ælfric's translation of Exodus, including his English translation of the Ten Commandments. These fragments, whose provenance remains unknown, were purchased by William S. Glazier for his distinguished manuscript collection (MS 11) and later entrusted to The Pierpont Morgan Library in 1963, after his death. In addition, sometime in the late fifties, Herbert Reichner of Stockbridge, Massachusetts, acquired a fragment of Ælfric's *Grammar*, which was once in the Royal Hohenzollern Library at Sigmaringen, and which he sold in 1961 to The Lilly Library at Indiana University, by this time the owner of the fragments purchased by Poole in 1947.

In 1965, at a Sotheby sale, the London dealer Quaritch bought two fragmentary strips of Anglo-Saxon for the James Marshall and Marie-Louise Osborn Collection at New Haven (MS 3a). These two pieces preserved parts of Ælfric's *Catholic Homilies* and, quite unexpectedly, proved to be from the same codex as the fragments from Ælfric's *Lives of Saints* originally purchased by Poole (MS 3b).

Nineteen sixty-nine was another notable year in the westward movement of early English manuscripts. In November, Yale University purchased twenty-eight more leaves of Aldhelm's *De laudibus virginitatis* from a Phillipps sale in London (MS 1a). These leaves, parts of the same original codex as the Lewis fragment (MS 1b) and the two leaves offered by Kraus in 1961, contain 189 Anglo-Saxon glosses. In December, H. P. Kraus, bidding for The Scheide Library, bought the Will of Æþelgifu, an immense single parchment and the largest known Anglo-Saxon will (MS 9).

And last, at least for the time being, Yale University in 1975 purchased a fragment of one leaf of St. Mark's Gospel from the London sale of the collection of Major J. R. Abbey of Storrington, Sussex (MS 2).

There are no fragments of Anglo-Saxon poetry in America, but the genres of prose are well represented. The homily is admirably exemplified in the Blickling codex in The Scheide Library (MS 8). And other fragments around the country have made the glories of this great manuscript all the more clear. The Osborn fragments in New Haven (MS 3a) preserve parts of Ælfric's homily on Palm Sunday; one of the leaves discovered in Kansas (MS 7) preserves parts of Ælfric's homily *De Uno Confessore*. The hagiography, a closely related genre, is represented in the Poole fragments at Indiana (MS 3b) which show parts of the lives of St. Apollonaris and Kings Abdon and Sennes. Biblical translations are represented both in the Glazier

17

fragments of Exodus (MS 11) and in the Yale fragments of Mark (MS 2). The prose legend of the cross on one of the Kansas discoveries (MS 6) represents still another kind of literary genre. Anglo-Saxon readers and scholars were devoted to making glossaries, and the University of Kansas has one leaf from one of the greatest surviving glossaries (MS 5); in addition, interlinear Anglo-Saxon glosses can be seen in the Morgan Library's Blickling Psalter (MS 10) and in the Aldhelm fragments at Yale (MS 1a) and Philadelphia (MS 1b). The first attempt at a grammar for Englishmen is represented by the Indiana fragment of Ælfric's *Grammar* (MS 4). And the Will of Æþelgifu (MS 9) in The Scheide Library is the most interesting known example of its kind.

Ælfric, the most prolific writer of the late tenth century, is, thus, represented by fragments of the Old Testament and a fragment of his *Grammar*; examples of his homilies and his lives of saints are also present. It is particularly fitting that Ælfric, a precise and highly orthodox theologian, be amply represented wherever the Blickling Homilies are preserved, for their occasionally "original" and unorthodox theology exemplified the sort of thing which he tried hard to correct.

Most of the manuscripts shown here were written in the late tenth or early eleventh century in clear insular minuscule. The notable exceptions are the eighth-century Psalter in the Morgan Library and the Aldhelm fragments. The principal hand in the Psalter (MS 8) is a majuscule, but most of the glosses (over seven hundred) are tenth-century and minuscule; twenty-one, however, are earlier, late eighth- or early ninth-century. The Aldhelm fragments (MS 1a and b) are parts of an early ninth-century manuscript, but again the glosses are from the tenth. Slight exceptions in date on the other end of the scale are the two leaves discovered in Kansas (MSS 6 and 7); N. R. Ker dates these closer to the middle of the eleventh century.

These precious fragments, especially when juxtaposed with the Blickling Homilies and Psalter and the Will of Æþelgifu, offer clear testimony on the fragility of the records of civilization. The Osborn fragments (MS 3a) and the Poole fragments (MS 3b) were once part of an immense manuscript of Ælfric's homilies and hagiographies.

18

Two other fragments from this codex survive in England but the surviving remnants amount to no more than two full leaves from what was once probably well over two hundred. The Kansas glossary fragment (MS 5) was once clearly a part of The British Library MS Harley 3376 but gives evidence that the original was much larger than what we now have. Similarly, the Kansas fragment of Ælfric's homily (MS 7) seems once to have been a part of Bodleian Library MS Hatton 115. The fragment of Ælfric's *Grammar* (MS 4) and a bifolium in the Bagford collection of fragments in The British Library are all that is now left of what was once a full codex. A similar situation applies with the Kansas fragment of the Cross Legend (MS 6); this fragment and two strips in the library of Corpus Christi College, Cambridge, are all that now remains of a much larger whole. The Aldhelm leaves (MSS 1a and b) survive in greater numbers but also testify to the mindless dispersal of great treasures. Even the great codices, the Blickling Psalter and the Blickling Homilies, have been mutilated; the former by missing leaves and the latter both by missing leaves and greatly trimmed margins. The Will of Æþelgifu seems to be the only one of these manuscripts which has not suffered significant mutilation. And this proportion is scarcely different from that shown in the general corpus of manuscripts containing Anglo-Saxon.

The clarity of Anglo-Saxon handwriting and the care of the Anglo-Saxon scholars for the records of civilization make us pause in wonder that their own records have been so shabbily treated. By the time of the English Renaissance, the Anglo-Saxon manuscripts were owned by monastic establishments which faced dissolution. And in the subsequent destruction and dispersal of artifacts many manuscripts seemed more valuable for their strong parchment than for anything written upon them. Throughout the sixteenth and early seventeenth centuries many an Anglo-Saxon codex was systematically pulled apart, cut into strips, and used by bookbinders for endpapers, pastedowns, binding strips to hold the boards to the spine, or for padding on the boards. Indeed, our American fragments of Anglo-Saxon owe their very survival today to their crude preservation as practical parts of Renaissance books. The Glazier fragments (MS 11) and the Abbey fragment now at Yale (MS 2) seem to have been used as endpapers. The Lewis fragment of Aldhelm (MS 1b) seems to have been made into a binding for a pamphlet. The Kansas glossary fragment (MS 5) was probably a pastedown. The *Grammar* fragment at Indiana (MS 4) and the Osborn and Poole fragments (MSS 3a and b) were definitely binding strips. And the fragments discovered in Kansas (MSS 6 and 7) had been used as padding along the boards.

Despite the glories of the Blickling Homilies, the Blickling Psalter, and the Will of Æþelgifu, the collection of American manuscripts containing Anglo-Saxon is meager indeed compared with those of The British Library, The Bodleian Library, or the Library at Corpus Christi College. This gathering of thirteen manuscripts, however, marks a number of important events. Several manuscripts here shown were not known at the time Dr. Ker made his *Catalogue* and, consequently, have no number in his list: the Osborn fragments (MS 3a), the Poole fragments (MS 3b), the Kansas discoveries (MSS 6 and 7), the Will of Æþelgifu (MS 9), and the Glazier fragments (MS 11). Peter Clemoes had made an hypothesis, on the basis of two fragments in Cambridge (Ker 81), that fragments like the Poole fragments might exist, but their existence was not made known until 1960. Dr. Ker knew that the Kansas glossary leaf probably existed and that it was a part of his no. 240 but he did not know where it was. Furthermore, several manuscripts known to Ker have come to America since his *Catalogue* was published: the *Grammar* fragment (MS 4; Ker 384), now also known to be part of the same codex as Ker 242, has moved from Sigmaringen to Bloomington, Indiana. The fragments of Mark (MS 2; Ker 1) have moved from the Abbey collection in Sussex to Yale, and the Aldhelm leaves in the Phillipps collection (MS 1a; part of Ker 12) have also moved to New Haven; in addition, the Lewis leaf in Philadelphia (MS 1b) is now recognized as a part of the same original codex as Ker 12.

While the Osborn fragments (MS 3a) and the Poole fragments (MS 3b) were once parts of the same codex, this exhibition marks the first time they have been close to each other since the book of which they were a part was destroyed in the early sixteenth century. Similarly, the Aldhelm fragments at Yale (MS 1a) and the Aldhelm fragment at Philadelphia (MS 1b) are side by side for the first time since the early nineteenth century. Curiously, also, two of the Aldhelm leaves at Yale (MS 401A of our MS 1a) and the Poole fragments at Indiana (MS 3b) were near each other once before, when they both were sold as parts of lot 1111 in the famous Libri sale on 5 April 1859. The Kansas glossary leaf (MS 5) is also once again their near neighbor, for it was part of lot 1118 in Libri's dispersal.

Thirteen manuscripts do not manifest a whole civilization, but they show clearly the Anglo-Saxon devotion to learning, to imaginative Christian literature, to orderliness, to clear handwriting, and to the preservation of the records of the past. We value their records, however fragmentary, as a vital part of our own heritage: linguistic, legal, literary, and religious.

THE MANUSCRIPTS

1a

Connecticut, New Haven
Yale University Library, Beinecke Library
  MSS 401 and 401a
Glosses to Aldhelm, *De laudibus virginitatis*
Fragments: twenty-eight leaves; IXc.;
  glosses, late Xc.

Cambridge University Library
  MS Add. 3330 (2 leaves) +
  Oxford, Bodl. Lib. MS Lat. th.
  d. 24, fols. 1–2 + W. Merton
  MS 41 (2 leaves); Ker 12

1b

Pennsylvania, Philadelphia
The Free Library of Philadelphia
John Frederick Lewis Collection, MS ET 121
Glosses to Aldhelm, *De laudibus virginitatis*
Fragment: one leaf; IXc.; glosses, late Xc.

2

Connecticut, New Haven
Yale University Library, Beinecke Library
  MS 578
Bible, N.T., *Gospel according to St. Mark,*
  West-Saxon translation
Fragment: one leaf; XIc.

3a

Connecticut, New Haven
Yale University Library, Beinecke Library
James Marshall and Marie-Louise Osborn
  Collection
Ælfric, *Catholic Homilies I, Homily for Palm
  Sunday*
Fragments: two strips; early XIc.

Oxford, Bodl. Lib. MS Eng. th.
  c. 74 (1 strip)
Cambridge, Queens' College
  MS Horne 75; Ker 81 (2
  strips)

3b

Indiana, Bloomington
Indiana University Library, The Lilly
  Library
George A. Poole, Jr., Collection, MS 10
Ælfric, *Lives of Saints, Lives of St. Apollonaris
  and Kings Abdon and Sennes*
Fragments: two strips; early XIc.

4

Indiana, Bloomington
Indiana University Library, The Lilly
  Library, Additional MS 1000
Ælfric, *Grammar*
Fragment: one strip; early XIc.

London, British Library MS
  Harley 5915, fols. 8–9; Ker
  242 (1 strip)

5

Kansas, Lawrence
University of Kansas Library
Kenneth Spencer Research Library, Pryce
  MS P2A:1
Glossary
Fragment: one leaf; ca. 1000

London, British Library MS
  Harley 3376 + Oxford, Bodl.
  Lib. MS Lat. Misc. a. 3, fol.
  49; Ker 240 (102 leaves)

6

Kansas, Lawrence
University of Kansas Library
Kenneth Spencer Research Library, Pryce
  MS C2:1
The Legend of the Cross
Fragment: one leaf; XIc.

Cambridge, Corpus Christi Coll.
  MS 557; Ker 73 (2 strips)

7

Kansas, Lawrence
University of Kansas Library
Kenneth Spencer Research Library, Pryce
  MS C2:2
Ælfric, Homily: *De Uno Confessore*
Fragment: one leaf; XIc.

Oxford, Bodl. Lib. MS Hatton
  115; Ker 332 (164 leaves)

8

New Jersey, Princeton
Princeton University Library
The Scheide Library, MS 71
The Blickling Homilies
xi+139 leaves; Xc.; prefatory, XVc. and
  XIVc.

9

New Jersey, Princeton
Princeton University Library
The Scheide Library
The Will of Æþelgifu
One leaf; late Xc.

10
New York, New York
The Pierpont Morgan Library, M. 776
Glosses to The Blickling Psalter
iii+88+i leaves; VIIIc.; glosses, ca. 800
   and Xc.; prefatory and closing, XVc.

11
New York, New York
The Pierpont Morgan Library
William S. Glazier Collection, G. 63
Ælfric, trans., Bible, O.T., *Heptateuch,*
   Exodus
Fragments: four leaves; XIc.

LOST MANUSCRIPTS

1
Illinois, Chicago
Library of Coella Lindsay Ricketts
Constitutional treatise on the Kingdom of the Franks
Fragment: one leaf

2
Illinois, Chicago
Library of Coella Lindsay Ricketts
Saint's Life
Fragment: one leaf

 Ia

Glosses to Aldhelm, *De laudibus virginitatis*

MSS 401 and 401A, Beinecke Library, Yale University, New Haven, Connecticut
Fragments: twenty-eight leaves; IXc.; glosses, late Xc.

DESCRIPTION

Twenty-six vellum leaves, known as MS 401, measuring generally 198 by 146 mm. (varying from 193 to 202 mm. vertically and from 141 to 148 mm. horizontally, except leaves 8 and 9 which have been radically trimmed from the outer and lower edges to 145 mm. by 102 and 105 mm. respectively), gathered irregularly (and erroneously) as follows: 1–5 (1 and 5 and 2 and 4 are conjugate), 6 and 7 (conjugate), 8 and 9 (conjugate), 10–16 (10 and 16, 12 and 15, and 13 and 14 are conjugate), 17–19 (17 and 19 are conjugate), 20, 21–26 (21 and 26, 23 and 24 are conjugate). The proper order, first outlined by Napier, should be 1–7, 9, 8 (reversing that bifolium), 10–20, 22, 21, 23–26. Hair and flesh sides are arranged irregularly (and would not be made regular by the correct arrangement of leaves), although there is a tendency for hair to face flesh within each half of a gathering. Ruling is generally from the flesh side and elaborate. Fols. 1–5 are ruled for nineteen lines of text; 10–26 are ruled for twenty-two lines, although 14v, 15r, and 23v have a partial twenty-third line. Two rules were made for each line (one for tops of letters as well) and there are two bounding lines on each side. The entire grid, whether for nineteen or twenty-two lines, measures about 140 by 110 mm. Prickings survive in the outer bounding line on both right and left; margins are wide, indicating that the manuscript has probably not been trimmed (the two vernacular glosses written at the top of fol. 7r are partly missing, indicating that some small trimmings may have taken place, at least on this leaf). There is water damage on many leaves, particularly serious on 19r–20v and on 26r where the writing has been restored by a later scribe. The leaves were simply bound in boards covered with brown paper, with white endpapers, while in the Phillipps Collection.

Two vellum leaves, a conjugate pair, known as MS 401A, 177 by 118 mm.,

29

are trimmed on outer edge so severely that some bits of text are lost. Ruled from the flesh side (the outer side) for twenty-two lines of text; the prickings, linings, etc. are identical with the twenty-two-line grid described above. These two leaves have also been trimmed top and bottom and punctured with three pairs of holes on each side of the center fold, for use as a binding.

All twenty-eight leaves are written in a brownish ink with a few decorated initials and other capitals touched with silver. There are at least two scribes, possibly more, although the two leaves of MS 401A seem all to have been done by a single hand. Lowe has observed that the script is probably ninth-century and possibly from Worcester or Canterbury.

TEXT

St. Aldhelm's work, *De laudibus virginitatis*, was written in the late seventh or early eighth century as a tribute to the virtue of chastity; ample illustrations are given from the lives of early Christians. Aldhelm wrote the book as part of his ecclesiastical development of Wessex (he was Bishop of Sherbourne, later Sarum, or Salisbury) and addressed it to the Abbess of Barking, St. Hildilitha, and a group of her nuns; in this context, his tract can be seen as an early statement of the important place of women in the church. The complete text is in Migne, *Patrologia Latina* LXXXIX, cols. 103–62. Comparison with the full text indicates that the thirty-five known leaves of this codex preserve over a third of the original work.

MS 401 was given great attention by several (but at least two) late tenth- or early eleventh-century readers who left behind numerous vernacular glosses as well as several Latin glosses. The vernacular glosses were published by Napier, who identified them as Kentish. Of the fifty-two pages, some nineteen show no Old English glosses at all; on others the glossing can be rather heavy. On several there are just a few, but on 7r there are twenty-two vernacular glosses and two others at the very top of the page. There are also a few dry point, or "scratched" glosses, done with the stylus and no ink; they are not easy to see but at least four can be found: fol. 4r at the end of l. 10, fol. 4v at the end of l. 5, fol. 5v above l. 1 and below the left corner of text. MS 401A has no glosses.

PROVENANCE

MSS 401 and 401A were grouped as lot 442 in the fifth part of the great sale of the medieval manuscripts of Sir Thomas Phillipps. On 25 November 1969 they were sold to H. P. Kraus who purchased them for Yale University. In the Phillipps Collection they were known as MS 8071 (26 fols.) and MS 20688 (2 fols.) and they had come to Phillipps in quite different ways.

In 1827 Samuel Weller Singer, Librarian to the Royal Institution, acquired the twenty-six-leaf group and gave one (fol. 22) to Phillipps. The remaining twenty-five leaves turned up as lot 32 in the Heber sale in February 1836, where Phillipps bought them and, uniting them with his single leaf, bound them all as MS 8071.

Over twenty years later Phillipps bought a group of fragments at the famous Libri sale, 5 April 1859; among these were two other leaves of his Aldhelm (MS 401A) which he catalogued separately as fols. 9 and 10 of MS 20688.

Part of Ker 12.

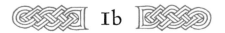

Glosses to Aldhelm, *De laudibus virginitatis*

MS ET 121, John Frederick Lewis Collection, The Free Library of Philadelphia, Philadelphia, Pennsylvania

Fragment: one leaf; IXc.; glosses, late Xc.

DESCRIPTION

This single vellum leaf, 193 mm. (varying from 189 at outer edge to 196 mm. at spine edge) by 142 mm., is ruled from the recto (which is the hair side) for twenty-two lines of text. Prickings survive on both the right and the left and set up a grid for writing (including two bounding lines on each side) which is 140 by 106 mm. The leaf was once folded in half (horizontally) between lines 12 and 13; there are four holes above the fold which are aligned perfectly with four below; each set of four is in two groups of two, starting 19 mm. from each outer edge with the second hole on toward the center of the leaf. The two rows of aligned holes, which are equidistant from the fold and 11 mm. from each other, suggest that this leaf may well have been used, or prepared for use, as a binding for a booklet.

The principal hand is probably ninth-century minuscule with one ornamental initial, *G* at line 12, recto, and eight letters lightly decorated with silver. There are seven Old English glosses to the text, two on the recto and five on the verso, in a small, somewhat timid, and often sloping minuscule hand of the late tenth or early eleventh century.

TEXT

St. Aldhelm's prose tract, *De laudibus virginitatis*, the principal text of the Lewis fragment, is an important work of the Anglo-Saxon period (see 1a, above). Its popularity and importance are at least partially attested by its being at least lightly glossed by a later reader. On the recto,

to *glosses* ad		(l. 7)
gemene, ceremonias		(l. 8)

On the verso,

bære, uehiculo	(l. 5)
gewin, tirocinium	(l. 9)
weredum, cateruis	(ll. 13–14)
færlicu, fortuitis	(l. 17)
gelimpum, cæsibus	(l. 18)

While these glosses on this fragment do not add any new words to the Anglo-Saxon lexicon, they have never been published before and should be considered alongside the Aldhelm glosses previously published by Napier and Meritt.

PROVENANCE

The Philadelphia collector John Frederick Lewis (1860–1932) acquired this leaf in 1914 and so noted in his own hand in the upper right-hand corner of the recto. Below Mr. Lewis's note is written, in another hand, "Given me by Mr. R. Contan / Mar. 1855." (The name could be Conitan, though the *i* would have no dot, or Comtan.) The links between Mr. C., that person to whom he gave the leaf, and Mr. Lewis are not known. At Mr. Lewis's death, his widow presented his collection of European and Oriental manuscripts to The Free Library of Philadelphia.

DeRicci *Supplement*, p. 454, XXIV:1.

*   *   *

Napier established that the twenty-six leaves of MS Phillipps 8071 and the two leaves in Cambridge University Library known as MS Add. 3330 were once parts of the same original Aldhelm manuscript. E. A. Lowe demonstrated that Bodl. Lib. MS Lat. th. d. 24, fol. 2, MS Phillipps 20688, fols. 9 and 10, and MS 41 (a bifolium) in the collection of Wilfred Merton were also once parts of this same codex. These five separate manuscripts, thirty-three leaves in all, were described (along with a second leaf at Oxford) as Ker 12 for the "over 200" Old English glosses they preserved to Aldhelm's text; and this original copy of *De laudibus virginitatis* could be shown to have once probably been a codex of nearly ninety-five leaves. If there once were nearly three times as many leaves, were there once nearly three times as many glosses?

On fol. 22 of MS 401 (formerly Phillipps 8071) are two notes which tell a good bit about the dispersal of this important codex. This leaf was "Preserved from the cover of a book by Singer, Librarian to the Royal Institution, and

33

by him presented to Sir Thomas Phillipps, Bart., 1827." Phillipps himself further records at the bottom of the leaf, "This leaf was given me by Mr. Singer. The others I bought at Heber's Sale, 1836." Ker observes that a note in the Cambridge University Library catalogue of Additional Manuscripts indicates that all of MS 8071 was found by Singer "in a bookseller's shop where it was being used to form the wrappers of books." Evidently, thus, Singer rescued some twenty-six leaves from destruction by a bookseller, gave one (fol. 22) to Phillipps in 1827, and ultimately disposed of the others so they were later sold as lot 32 in the eleventh part of the Heber sale, on 10 February 1836 and the following days; they were bought there by Phillipps for £20. 9s. 6d., and then joined with his earlier single leaf. Singer probably considered fol. 22 a separable item because it had been folded horizontally across the middle and punched with parallel pairs of holes on each side of the fold for use as a binding.

Ker records that the origin of the two Cambridge leaves (MS Add. 3330) reflects their part in this same dispersal. The first of the two leaves "was the wrapper of N. Bownde, *Unbeliefe of St. Thomas* (8vo, A.D. 1608) which was bought by the librarian, Francis Jenkinson, from Mr. Bohn of Brighton, 7 December 1889." The second leaf was also purchased by Mr. Jenkinson, as one among several separate fragments, from Mr. W. V. Daniell of London and was made a part of the Cambridge library on 10 March 1898; it, too, had "evidently been used in binding."

Ker further records that both of the leaves at Oxford (Bodl. Lib. MS Lat. th. d. 24, fols. 1 and 2) "have been wrappers of small books," although one was catalogued in 1895 and the other came to the Bodleian only when presented in 1942 by H. W. Garrod. Both Meritt and Ker note that the Oxford leaves preserve no glosses.

The leaves in Mr. Merton's collection, a bifolium, elegantly bound in orange morocco by C. C. McLeish, seem not to have been damaged further than in their separation from the main codex. Ker records that Mr. Merton bought the conjugate pair from Tregaskis in 1931. H. P. Kraus offered these leaves for sale in Catalogue 88, *Fifty Medieval and Renaissance Manuscripts* (1958), as no. 5 (pp. 11–13), and again in Catalogue 95, *Twenty-five Manuscripts* (1961), as no. 3 (pp. 13–15). When they were sold, they returned to Europe.

The Lewis Aldhelm leaf was first associated with these other parts of the original codex by the cataloguer who prepared part five of Sotheby's sale of Phillipps manuscripts in 1969. The fold across the middle and the holes alongside the fold-mark make it plain that the Lewis fragment was indeed used as a binding for a pamphlet and was rescued for preservation apparently in the same way as both leaves at Cambridge and both leaves at Oxford.

At the Guglielmo Libri sale, 5 April 1859, Sir Thomas Phillips bought lot 1111 (see also MS 3b, below), a "Collection of Latin Fragments, written by Anglo-Saxon Scribes during the eighth and ninth centuries," with "some of the smallest fragments being also in the Anglo-Saxon language." This group contained two leaves which were arranged in his collection as fols. 9 and 10 of MS 20688. These two leaves were not only separated from the main book but trimmed on all sides before being crudely used as a binder. When the sales of Sir Thomas Phillipps's manuscripts were in preparation in the nineteen-sixties, these two leaves from MS 20688 were rightly joined with the twenty-six leaves of MS 8071 as a single unit, lot 442. They were purchased by H. P. Kraus for the Bienecke Library.

Thus, thirty-five known leaves (twenty-eight at Yale, two at Cambridge, two at Oxford, one in Philadelphia, and two once in New York but now sold to a European collector) remain from an important ninth-century manuscript of Aldhelm's *De laudibus virginitatis*, a rather elegant manuscript of about ninety-five leaves which was carefully read and studied by scholars for at least two hundred years after its composition. The leaves from Yale and the leaf from Philadelphia are reunited in this exhibition for the first time since at least the early nineteenth century.

Bible, N.T., *Gospel According to St. Mark,* West-Saxon translation

MS 578, Beinecke Library, Yale University, New Haven, Connecticut
Fragment: part of one leaf; XIc.

DESCRIPTION

Part of a single leaf, trimmed on all sides; the leaf was folded horizontally in the middle and attached at the fold as an endpaper at the back of a fourteenth-century Psalter. The upper half was used as a pastedown and the lower as the back flyleaf. The upper half is badly damaged; only about an eighth of it still survives, and this in shreds, although now free from the board. The surviving lower half measures 93 mm. vertically (varying from 90 on the right to 96 on the left) and 143 mm. horizontally. The longest vertical extension of the shreds of the upper half is about 42 mm.; the longest horizontal extension is 102 mm. As trimmed for use in the binding, the leaf would have been around 186 by 143 mm. The ruling (which is not used as the base line for the script) is from the recto which is the hair side. Parts of fifteen lines survive: fragmentary bits from six lines on the upper half and nine lines on the lower. A small hole in the middle of the sixth line of the lower half has disposed of a letter or two from both recto and verso.

The original leaf was probably long enough for the Gospel passage to have continued without interval from the recto to the verso. With the trimming of the lower edge and the serious damage to the upper half, it is difficult to say, however, just what the additional dimensions were. We can be sure that there was at least one more line of text at the bottom of the leaf, for some of the ascenders survive on the verso. The original leaf, if ruled for as many as seventeen or eighteen lines of text, would have preserved a complete text of, say, St. Mark 1:23–43, and, with reasonable margins, could have been as much as 250 by 215 mm.

Ker dates the hand as eleventh-century and characterizes it as "angular" but "rather sprawling." The dialect is West-Saxon, although, as Ker points out, there are spelling variants from more expected forms.

The trimmed leaf once contained all of *St. Mark* 1:24–31 and 36–42, although much is now lost because of the shredding of the upper half and the trimming. Verses 27–31 are fairly well preserved on the recto of the lower half and verses 39–42 on the verso. Verse 29 is introduced by the Latin quotation, written in the same hand: "Et *pro*tinus egredientes de sinagoga uenerunt *in* d. . . ." The Latin is the same as the vernacular text of *Mark* 1:27 which follows immediately. Similarly, on the verso, the Latin beginning of verse 40 is written immediately before the Old English text, but in this instance the Latin is clearly added later, even though in another insular hand. In addition, a rubric for verse 40 is crowded in, in an entirely different hand, between the last two lines of verse 39: "þis godspel gebyra𝔡 on wodnesdæg on þære fifteoðan wucan ofer pe[ntecosten]," but the color is badly smudged and the reading is dependent on Ker. The Latin introductory quotations and the interpolated rubric led the cataloguer at Sotheby's to describe this leaf as part of a lectionary, but since there is no evidence that the text was *not* complete and since the rubric and at least one of the Latin tags were definitely added later, this leaf was probably once part of a full and continuous Gospel text, later annotated for devotional uses.

PROVENANCE

In all probability, the Anglo-Saxon Bible of which this fragment was once a part came to pieces some time before the binding of the fourteenth-century Psalter in which it was used. The book was owned in the sixteenth century by Wyllyam Medlycott, Wyllyam Emey, and Wyllyam Hendeley and in the seventeenth by Johannes Browne, or at least these gentlemen felt bold enough to write their names in the book. In the nineteen-twenties it was owned by Sir Sidney Cockerell and passed from him to the collection of Mr. C. H. St. John Hornby where it was known as MS 70. Major John Roland Abbey of Storrington, Sussex, purchased it from Hornby and catalogued it in his collection as MS J.A. 3243. The Psalter and flyleaf were sold as item 2955 in the ninth part of Sotheby's sale of Abbey's collection on 25 March 1975 and were purchased by Yale University.

Ker 1.

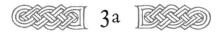

Ælfric, *Catholic Homilies I, Homily for Palm Sunday*

James Marshall and Marie-Louise Osborn Collection, Beinecke Library,
Yale University, New Haven, Connecticut
Fragments: two strips; early XIc.

DESCRIPTION

These two vellum strips were once parts of a single leaf written in the early
eleventh century. They were cut vertically from its left side and represented
about half the original leaf, but later the tops of both strips were also cut off.
Strip *a* is 255 mm. by 42 mm.; strip *b* has an average length of 259 mm.
(varying from 252 to 263 mm.) and is 43 mm. wide. Deep stains and holes indicate use in a bookbinding; strip *a* was lapped over strip *b* to hold the top
board to the spine of the book. The recto is the hair side of the vellum. The
original strips were about 300 mm. long and were ruled for thirty-two lines
of text.

TEXT

These fragmentary lines (27 on each side of *a*; 28 on each side of *b*) preserve
parts of Ælfric's homily for Palm Sunday in his First Series of the *Catholic
Homilies* (*The Homilies of the Anglo-Saxon Church . . . the Sermones Catholici, or
Homilies of Ælfric*, ed. Benjamin Thorpe [2 vols., London, 1844–46], I, XIV).
Ælfric here cites Jesus's order to fetch an ass and its foal to begin the proces-
sion into Jerusalem. His interpretation dilates on the meaning of the two men
sent for the asses, the fact that the asses were tied, the master of the asses who
questioned that they should be taken, and the two asses themselves.

PROVENANCE

In the second or third decade of the sixteenth century, the codex of which
these fragments were once parts was, in all probability, pulled apart in the
London bookbindery of a craftsman now known only by the initials "K. L. –
L. K." These two strips were used to attach the front binding board to the

spine of Augustine's *Sermones* (Paris, 1520) and there they stayed until the book, in the possession of the presbytery library at Winchester, gradually deteriorated. The front board, with the fragments attached, fell away from the book and was subsequently found in a rubbish heap by Dr. James Molloy. He removed the fragments and they were sold as a pair on 29 July 1965 at Sotheby's as lot 576 and were bought by Quaritch for the Osborn Collection.

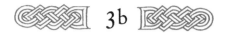 3^b

Ælfric, *Lives of Saints, Lives of St. Apollonaris and Kings Abdon and Sennes*

MS 10, George A. Poole, Jr., Collection, The Lilly Library,
Indiana University, Bloomington, Indiana
Fragments: two strips; early XIc.

DESCRIPTION

These two vellum strips represent about half of a single leaf originally written near the beginning of the eleventh century. These two strips, now re-sewn into their original contiguous position, were cut from the left side of the original leaf for use in a bookbinding. Each strip is 282 mm. long and the two, as re-sewn, have, in combination, an average width of 78 mm. (varying from 76 to 82 mm.). Stains and holes show the placement of the vellum to join binding boards to the book itself. The recto is the hair side of the vellum.

TEXT

The thirty-two fragmentary lines on each side preserve parts of the ending of Ælfric's life of St. Apollonaris and parts of his account of the martyrdom of Kings Abdon and Sennes and the epistle to Abgarus (*Lives of Saints*, ed. Walter W. Skeat [2 vols., London, 1881–1900], nos. XXII and XXIV). The end of St. Apollonaris's life records his fiery speeches to the heathen judge Demosthenes, his escape through the offices of a kindly (and secretly Christian) centurion, his immediate recapture, his suffering at the hands of the heathen, his final words of prophecy, his death and burial. The next fragmentary account describes the fruitless efforts of the wicked Emperor Decius and his cruel henchman Valerian to force the good Kings Abdon and Sennes to make sacrifices to heathen gods. The saints survive whips and beasts and so enrage the ruler and judge by their goodness that their execution is prescribed and instantly carried out. The fragments close with a few words from the beginning of Christ's letter to Abgarus.

40

In all probability, these strips were cut away from the original leaf in the London bindery of "K. L. – L. K." between 1510 and 1530. The book in which they were used is not known, but by 28 March 1859 the fragments were described as a part of lot 1111 in the Libri sale. They were bought by Sir Thomas Phillipps and became lot 22229 in his collection when it was sold in 1947, through Messrs. Robinson of Pall Mall, to George A. Poole, Jr., of Chicago. In 1958, The Lilly Library acquired the Poole collection.

DeRicci *Supplement*, p. 181, no. 40.

*   *   *

The New Haven fragments (3a) and the Bloomington fragments (3b) were once parts of a single large closely written codex which contained both Ælfric's *Lives of Saints* and his *Catholic Homilies* (at least a goodly part of Series I). The leaves of this codex measured approximately 300 mm. vertically and were generally ruled for thirty-two lines of text, the written space having a vertical measurement between 250 and 255 mm. Other fragments from this codex survive in British libraries.

The library of Queens' College, Cambridge, owns two strips (known as MS Horne 75), each 302 mm. long, which are intimately related to the Bloomington fragments. Strip *a* of Horne 75 preserves parts of Ælfric's life of St. Apollonaris (Skeat xxiv) and was cut from the leaf which, in the original codex, came immediately before the leaf from which the Bloomington fragments were cut. Strip *b* of MS Horne 75 preserves parts of Ælfric's account of Christ's letter to Abgarus which immediately follows the parts on the verso of the Bloomington fragments. Indeed, it is clear that strip *b* of MS Horne 75 was cut from the extreme right side of the leaf which immediately followed, in the original codex, the leaf from which the Bloomington fragments were cut. Strip *b* goes on, after the Abgarus letter is finished, to include parts of Ælfric's account of the Maccabees (Skeat xxv).

The Bodleian Library at Oxford has a fragment, MS Eng. th. c. 74, which preserves parts of the end of Ælfric's homily for the second Sunday after Easter in the First Series of the *Catholic Homilies* (Thorpe I, xvii) and parts of the opening of his homily for Wednesday in Rogationtide, *De fide catholica* (Thorpe I, xx). This fragment was part of a leaf which measured between 290 and 300 mm. vertically. With slight variations, the handwriting and other palaeographic features identify this fragment as part of the same original codex from which were taken the fragments now at New Haven, Bloomington, and Cambridge.

The Cambridge fragments were discovered in 1953 by Dr. N. R. Ker in the binding of Hector Boece's *Historia scotorum* (Paris, 1527). The binding of the Boece was identified by Dr. Ker as "contemporary London work"; it was by the binder "K. L. – L. K." in the second or third decade of the sixteenth century. These fragments are described in his *Catalogue* (Oxford, 1957) as no. 81. The Oxford fragment was also discovered by Dr. Ker. He identified it in position as a binding strip along the lower board of a copy of Augustine's *Sermones* (Paris, 1520). This book had been in the presbytery library at Winchester for many years, had lost its upper board (see 3a, above), was sold to the London dealer Weinreb in 1966, and later appeared as lot 630 in Hodgson's sale on 20 January 1967, where it was spotted by Dr. Ker and secured for the Bodleian.

These seven fragments: two at New Haven, one at Oxford, two at Cambridge, and two at Bloomington, represent all that is now known to survive from what must have been an impressive Anglo-Saxon codex of the early eleventh century. This manuscript, the work of a single scribe, contained works by Ælfric, Abbot of Eynsham, both his major cycle of sermons, the *Catholic Homilies*, and his cycle of hagiographies. It was, in all probability, derived from a single source manuscript which was produced in the author's own scriptorium.

4

Ælfric, *Grammar*

Additional MS 1000, The Lilly Library, Indiana University,
Bloomington, Indiana
Fragment: one strip, early XIc.

DESCRIPTION

This fragment preserves approximately the lower two-thirds of a vertical strip
cut from the middle of a leaf written in the early eleventh century. The top
edge is jagged but the longest vertical extension is 198 mm.; the width is 62
mm. The original leaf contained twenty-six lines of text and the written space
measured about 208 by 115 mm. Stains and folds running vertically along the
fragment indicate that it was probably once used in a bookbinding to join a
board to the book proper.

TEXT

Ælfric's *Grammar* was a systematic translation and expansion of Priscian's
Institutiones Grammaticae. The resulting work is bilingual, for while it is primarily a translation of a Latin grammar, it juxtaposes vernacular examples
with Latin principles and forms. The nineteen fragmentary lines on the recto
of this fragment include parts of the discussion of irregular verbs, beginning
with the exposition of *eo*, and continuing through most of *sum;* the verso preserves parts of Ælfric's outlines of defective verbs, specifically parts of *ferio,
percutio, fero, furo, uescor,* and others.

PROVENANCE

This fragment was discovered in 1870 in a Düsseldorf book stall by A. Birlinger and shortly thereafter was acquired by the Fürstlich Hohenzollern'sche
Bibliothek at Sigmaringen, where it was then catalogued by Dr. N. R. Ker
as no. 384. The Lilly Library purchased the fragment in 1960 from Herbert
Reichner of Stockbridge, Massachusetts.

The bifolium known as fols. 8 and 9 of British Library MS Harley 5915

43

(Ker 242) was once a part of the same codex as the leaf from which the Indiana *Grammar* fragment was cut. The top of this bifolium has been cut away but it can be shown that each page was originally ruled for 26 lines of text and that the written space originally measured 208 mm. vertically and 116 mm. across. Since the handwriting and abbreviation patterns are also the same on both the Indiana fragment and the bifolium, their common origin is indisputable. A prominent brown vertical stain on the bifolium indicates that it, too, was probably used in a bookbinding, perhaps as a pastedown. In all probability these two fragments, once part of an elegantly written early eleventh-century codex of Ælfric's *Grammar*, first parted company when the manuscript was pulled apart by a bookbinder in search of sound vellum to strengthen his bindings.

Ker 384; DeRicci *Supplement,* p. 186, no. 132.

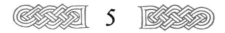

Glossary

Pryce MS P2A:1, Kenneth Spencer Research Library, University of Kansas,
Lawrence, Kansas
Fragment: one leaf; ca. 1000

DESCRIPTION

One vellum leaf, from around 1000, measuring 302 by 212 mm., ruled from
the recto for twenty lines of text in a grid measuring 199 by 80 mm. (with one
additional bounding line 10 mm. out from the grid on each side). The small
writing space is supplemented by many marginal notations and additions.
The outer margin is badly frayed; there is one large tear in the upper margin
near the outer edge; there is a large hole in the upper right center. These mu-
tilations and the prominent stains and deep creasings indicate that this leaf
may very well have been used in a bookbinding, possibly as a pastedown or
for padding.

TEXT

This fragment preserves part of a list of hard Latin words and phrases, beginning with "In superum mare" to "Interpolata reprobata." Several are ex-
plained by interlinear glosses in Old English; others by Latin glosses; others
are supplemented or clarified by marginalia. The more than twenty Old English glosses contain some otherwise undocumented words which have entered
the lexicon from this occurrence. H. D. Meritt found six new words here for
his 1960 supplement to Clark Hall's *Concise Anglo-Saxon Dictionary* and these
are discussed again in Alastair Campbell's addenda to the Bosworth-Toller
dictionary *Supplement*.

PROVENANCE

This leaf was originally part of the Harleian glossary of rare words (British
Library MS Harley 3376), catalogued by Dr. Ker as no. 240, with careful
notation of this missing leaf. Ker dates the glossary around 1000 and specu-

lates that the primary glossary manuscript had lost the two now separated leaves before it was acquired by Lord Harley in 1720. These two separate leaves were part of the Libri sale in 1859, when they were purchased by Sir Thomas Phillipps as lot 1118. They were subsequently sold by Messrs. Robinson in separate collections of fragments: one in 1953 to the Bodleian where it is known as Bodl. Lat. Misc. 2.3, fol. 49; the other in 1954 to Mr. Frank Glenn of Kansas City, who later that same year sold it to the University of Kansas.

The primary manuscript is arranged alphabetically and contains words from *Abacus* to problem words beginning with *f*. The Bodleian leaf contains words which start with *In* and preceded the Kansas leaf. Stains on the Bodleian leaf led Dr. Ker to suggest that it may have been used in a bookbinding. Thus, the evidence of the Bodleian leaf and the Kansas leaf suggests that the Harleian glossary may well have been much larger than its present limitation to words beginning with the first six letters of the alphabet.

The Kansas glossary fragment is slightly larger than the Bodleian fragment (which Ker measures as 295 by 205 mm.) and a good deal larger than the Harleian glossary (which Ker measures as ca. 212 by 148 mm.). But Dr. Ker has gathered evidence to prove the relationship of the separated leaves to the now much trimmed glossary.

Part of Ker 240.

6

The Legend of the Cross

Pryce MS C2:1, Kenneth Spencer Research Library, University of Kansas,
Lawrence, Kansas
Fragment: one leaf; XIc.

DESCRIPTION

This single leaf, measuring 220 by 165 mm., has been trimmed on both sides
(but without loss to the text) and on the top (with considerable loss). Twenty-
three full lines of text (with descenders of another) survive on both recto and
verso. The twenty-three extant lines of text measure about 185 mm. vertically; each line, thus, occupies slightly more than 8 mm. of space. Comparison with an analogous and full text of this legend published by Napier (MS
Bodley 343) indicates that four lines of text are missing from the top of the
verso. The twenty-seven original lines of text must, therefore, have taken a
vertical space of about 218 mm.; and, if the generous lower margin is any in-
dicator, the original leaf was probably about 270 by 200 mm. The leaf is ruled
with a dry stylus from the verso, which is the flesh side. At least one bounding
line can be seen right and left; a second on the left (verso) is about 8 mm. far-
ther out; the inner width of the grid is 115 mm.; no prickings have survived
the trimming.

The recto has been darkened and damaged by its prolonged contact with
the leather binding. The middle parts of many lines in the center of the page
can be read only with difficulty. However, the offset on the leather is often
clear and can be read with a mirror to fill in doubtful passages.

The script is an insular minuscule and has been identified by N. R. Ker as
the same as that shown on the two strips known as C.C.C.C. MS 557 (Ker
73), "a rather poor hand" of the mid-eleventh century. The glosses on both
have been identified by Ker and Colgrave as from the "tremulous" hand tra-
ditionally associated with Worcester. Punctuation is by mid-line point.

47

The Legend of the Cross has been carefully studied by A. S. Napier. He published a twelfth-century version of this text from MS Bodley 343 (E.E.T.S., o.s. 103, London, 1894) and assumed an earlier vernacular source, of which this fragment and the two strips known as C.C.C.C. MS 557 (Ker 73) have been identified (by Bertram Colgrave and Ann Hyde) as the sole survivors. The text preserved on the Kansas fragment gives some of the legendary, early history of the wood which formed the Cross; in Old Testament times it grew as the powerful rods of Moses; each of the deeds of Moses, therefore, requires special interpretation.

The "tremulous hand" of Worcester has provided several glosses to the text; some modify spelling; others give Latin words for the vernacular.

PROVENANCE

The eleventh-century manuscript, of which this fragment and the two strips known as C.C.C.C. MS 557 were once parts, was, in all probability, copied in the twelfth century to supply the text for *The Legend of the Cross* for MS Bodley 343. This eleventh-century manuscript was glossed in Worcester in the early thirteenth century by the famous "tremulous hand" and may have remained there until the destruction of monastic libraries. The codex was pulled apart at least by the sixteenth century, for, as Ker notes, the two strips of C.C.C.C. MS 557 were discovered in contemporary bindings of sixteenth-century books "bequeathed to Corpus Christi College by Archbishop Parker." Ker suggests that perhaps the two Cambridge strips were cut from "a discarded leaf of one of the Worcester manuscripts belonging to Parker: there is much evidence that Parker disliked loose ends and was at pains to destroy, erase, or cover up the remains of texts which either began or ended imperfectly, especially if they came first or last in a volume." Colgrave and Hyde extend this suspicion to the history of Pryce MS c2:1.

In the middle of the seventeenth century this leaf was trimmed on at least three sides (but radically on the top) to fit, recto out, as padding on the outside of a thin pasteboard used as the top board for a binding of Kingsmill Long's translation of *Barclay his Argenis* (London, 1636). In 1957, the University of Kansas, for the equivalent of twelve dollars, bought the Barclay at Pearson's Book Rooms in Cambridge. A few years later, Mr. John Siedzik, then curator of manuscripts at Kansas, noted that the leather was separating from the board and that a manuscript padding was visible. The fragment was removed by Max Adjarian of the Grolier Bindery in Mission, Kansas, so carefully that the offset can be clearly read on the inside of the leather binding. After removal, the fragment was numbered MS Y103 and thoroughly studied by Bertram Colgrave and Ann Hyde in 1961. It has since been renumbered as Pryce MS c2:1.

 7

Ælfric, Homily: *De Uno Confessore*

Pryce MS c2:2, Kenneth Spencer Research Library, University of Kansas,
Lawrence, Kansas
Fragment: one leaf; XIc.

DESCRIPTION

This single leaf, which measures 207 by 157 mm., has been trimmed across
the bottom (Colgrave and Hyde suspect also from the edges). Twenty-six
lines of text, and ascenders of a twenty-seventh, survive. Comparison with an
analogous text (C.C.C. MS 188; Ker 43, article 45) reveals that only one
line has been lost between the last surviving line on the recto and the first line
on the verso. The verso, which is the hair side, was ruled with a dry stylus for,
in all probability, twenty-seven lines of text. The grid measures 95 mm.
across; it probably once measured 192 vertically. Two bounding lines, 10
mm. apart, can be seen on the right and two, about 7 mm. apart, on the left.
Prickings for each of the bounding lines survive at the top. If the surviving
generous margins are indicative, the original leaf was probably about 245
mm. long and probably little wider than it now is.

The right side of the recto has been badly damaged from its long contact
with the leather cover of the binding. Parts of the damaged text can be clearly
read, however, with a mirror from their offset on the leather.

N. R. Ker has identified this leaf as one of the heretofore missing parts of
Bodleian Library MS Hatton 115 (Ker 332, article 24). Colgrave and Hyde
theorize, from the amount of text missing from Hatton 115, the quiring of the
original codex, and the number "3" at the top of the recto of this leaf, that
this was the third leaf of six removed from Hatton 115, the others of which
are apparently now lost.

The script, an insular minuscule of the latter eleventh century, has been
described fully by Ker (for Hatton 115) and by Colgrave and Hyde.

Ælfric wrote many homilies for use throughout the church year, but none so versatile as one from the Second Series of *Catholic Homilies* known as *In Natale Unius Confessoris* or *De Uno Confessore*. In this instance, the virtuous Christian martyr was not specifically named by Ælfric, but after the exposition of the parable of the talents, appropriate blanks were left for the discreet use of the preacher who was required to commemorate some less widely known worthy. The preacher reminds his listeners in this fragment that no one knows the time of the second coming and he exhorts his hearers to contemplate this good (but nameless) saint to help in proper preparation for the end.

The glosses on this text have also been identified by Colgrave and Hyde as from "the tremulous Worcester hand." The glosses are similar to those on Pryce MS c2:1; some change spelling and indicate pronunciation; others provide a few Latin synonyms.

PROVENANCE

Bodleian Library MS Hatton 115 has been dated by Ker from the latter half of the eleventh century. Ker also notes that this codex was glossed by the "tremulous hand" in Worcester in the first half of the thirteenth century. Christopher, Lord Hatton, had the manuscript before 1644; in 1675 it was moved to the Bodleian with other parts of his collection. A few leaves were taken from the codex, damaging more than one homily. This Kansas leaf was taken from the general homily on a confessor and later used in a seventeenth-century binding of Barclay's *Argenis*. The modern history of Pryce MS c2:2 (earlier y104) exactly parallels that of Pryce MS c2:1 (MS 6).

8

The Blickling Homilies

MS 71, The Scheide Library, Princeton University Library, Princeton, New Jersey
xi+139 leaves; Xc.; prefatory XVc. and XIVc.

DESCRIPTION

The Anglo-Saxon codex consists of 139 leaves, generally soft, thin, and polished, gathered as follows: 1^8, 2^{6+1} (before 1), 3^6, 4^8, 5^2, 6^8, 7^{10}, 8^{8+1} (before 1), 9^6, 10^{8+1} (after 5), 11^6, 12^{6+1} (before 2), $13-15^8$, 16^{8+1} (before 1), $17-18^8$, 19^4, and measuring 201 (ranging 198–209) by 150 mm. (ranging 147–155). All extant leaves have been trimmed, except on the binding edge, although much damage has been repaired, often by added vellum on corners or margins; water damage is evident throughout, but especially on fols. 9–10, 16–21, 29–31, 48–52, 73–74, 80–81, 84–87, 90–91, 98, 119–121, and 135.

All leaves were ruled with a dry stylus to form a grid for twenty-one lines of text, about 178 (ranging 170–185) by 98 mm. (ranging 97–101), with four vertical bounding lines, two right and two left (each pair being about 5–6 mm. apart), for capitals. Generally, the bounding lines and the top and bottom rules extend well beyond the grid proper. Ruling was usually done one sheet at a time and on the hair side; some prickings for the horizontal lines survive but none for the bounding lines.

The two principal hands, both insular minuscule, have been described carefully by Ker and exhaustively by Willard. Hand A dominates the first sixteen gatherings of the codex (fols. 1–119v), with nine separate but brief interruptions on fols. 50–119v by Hand B. From fol. 120 to the end of the codex, Hand B proceeds without interruption. Hand B wrote, in all, about eighteen percent of the codex. Hand A is somewhat squarer and heavier than B, with long descenders, especially on the last line of a page. Hand B has also done some of the titles for the homilies (for xvi and xvii), although probably three other hands seem to have been at work here as well. One seems to have done titles for Homilies ii–vii and ix; another, for xi–xiv; still another, for xv. Other eleventh-century hands have made additions and corrections to the

52

text: one expanded the comments in Homily XI on the date for the end of the world (fol. 72r); another went through Homily II inserting *se* before *Hælend*. Still other scribes, perhaps three to five, contributed to making the undistinguished initials.

The entire codex (but especially the first two-thirds) is annotated by many hands which record the history of Lincoln. About sixty-four percent of these records are from the fourteenth century; twenty-nine percent, from the fifteenth; five percent, from the sixteenth; and two percent, from the seventeenth. Several entries are not dated.

The arrangement of sheets in the quires is noteworthy because it is highly irregular. Sometimes it follows Ker's "normal" pattern in which "a hair side formed the outside of a quire and within the quire flesh faced flesh and hair faced hair." Gatherings 3, 12, 13, and 17, and perhaps 16 and 19, were in this pattern. Most of the other gatherings are not so regular and are clearly related to what Ker has described as an older insular pattern in which "all the hair sides faced outwards," and thus, inside a quire, hair faced flesh. None of the gatherings follows this pattern precisely, although twelve of the thirteen quires not yet mentioned (i.e., all except eighteen) exhibit the hair-flesh order in some form or, as in the case of five, the potential for it. Gathering 18 is a reversal of the "normal" pattern, i.e., starting with the flesh side out but continuing with hair facing hair and flesh facing flesh. Of the others, 1–2, 6–11, and 14–15 exhibit odd mixed arrangements, differing not only from Ker's two types but from each other. In Ker's *Catalogue* there are eleven manuscripts described with such irregularities, and nine of the eleven are dated tenth century or earlier. The strange and various arrangements of hair and flesh sides in this codex perhaps indicate that the homilist's dating of his composition in the year 971 (fol. 72r) is also an accurate date for the manuscript itself.

The leaves were numbered correctly in pencil in the middle of the right side of the recto by Rudolph Willard in 1956. Other signatures and paginations, one by Michael Maittaire, also survive.

Surviving signatures and the contents of the volume permit informed speculation about the original size of the book. The earliest signatures reveal that four gatherings are probably missing from the beginning, one more from between gatherings 9 and 10 and perhaps still another from between 3 and 4 (or 7 and 8, or 8 and 9). The fragmentary last homily shows clearly that one gathering is missing from the end of the codex; perhaps even more, since there very well could have been additional homilies. Individual leaves are missing

53

from between fols. 58 and 59, 64 and 65, 85 and 86, 135 and 136, and after 139. Thus, the original manuscript contained five more leaves than the surviving 139 and at least six more gatherings. If these gatherings were at all typical of this codex, they contained six or eight leaves. Thus, the original book would have contained, at the very least, 180 leaves (if the missing gatherings had but six leaves each) or, more probably, 192 (if all had eight). And, of course, if there were additional homilies at the end, the book would have been even bigger.

In addition to these lost gatherings, the manuscript was seriously trimmed, probably in the sixteenth century, for the sake of the vellum. The surviving leaves give some indication of their original size, however. Some lower margins are quite long (26 mm. on fol. 6r) and at least one upper margin is moderately generous (11 mm. on fol. 129). If these are indicative, the original leaves must have measured at least 215 mm. vertically (average height of grid, 178 mm., plus these two wide margins). This is a little larger than the present average vertical measurement of 201 mm. However, most of the early medieval signatures are completely trimmed and at least 10 mm. would be required for the signature and any decent space; thus, a more likely original vertical dimension is 225 mm. This means that two strips, each 12 mm. wide, could be taken from each leaf. But if the vellum strips were to be of any use, and thus worth the trimming, they would have to be at least 20 mm. wide. With this added length, the original vertical measurement of the leaves would have been around 241 mm., i.e., beyond the present 201 mm., 20 more for the top and 20 more for the bottom. The probable original lateral measurement can be similarly established as 170-175 mm. (20–25 more than the present average). The hypothetical original, which could have measured 241 by as much as 175 mm., would have surrounded the text on all sides with quite generous margins.

Nine leaves have been added to the beginning of the codex. The first six, of thick matte parchment in one gathering, measure 205 by 150 mm. The next two, a bifolium of more polished parchment, are somewhat smaller, 200 by 146 mm. The first six are mid-fifteenth-century; the next two, from the early fourteenth. A note by Benjamin Thorpe, dated 16 March 1843, has been tipped in at the end of the codex.

TEXT

Eighteen homilies, designed for use throughout the church year, are the principal texts of this codex. The first begins imperfectly, but seems to have been

54

planned for the Feast of the Annunciation; the second homily is intended for Quinquagesima; the third, fourth, fifth, and sixth, for later Sundays in Lent. The seventh homily is set for Easter. The eighth, ninth, and tenth homilies are intended for the three Rogation Days; the eleventh is for Ascension Day and the twelfth for Pentecost. The remaining homilies are devoted to fixed days of the church year: the assumption of St. Mary, the nativity of St. John the Baptist, the martyrdom of Sts. Peter and Paul, Michaelmas, Martinmas, and the day of St. Andrew.

The homilies are often vigorous expositions of eschatological themes (especially the homilies for Easter and Rogationtide). At least one (the ascension of St. Mary) is a confused conflation of two sources. Most have Latin sources, though some seem to have been derived directly from earlier vernacular translations. The homiliary is an anthology of diverse rhetorical exhortations, some skillful, some confused, some straightforward and orthodox, others rather imaginative and tending toward heresy.

The margins are filled with the records of the City of Lincoln, lists of officials and synopses of events, from the early fourteenth century to the beginning of the seventeenth, though most of the records are from the fourteenth and early fifteenth centuries.

The prefatory pages are a four-page calendar of the mid-fifteenth century, and a two-page series of quotations from the Gospels; both also have Lincoln marginalia.

PROVENANCE

The precise origin of the Blickling Homilies codex is unknown. Studies of the vocabulary have suggested an Anglian origin but the earliest precise date for its whereabouts is 1304. In that year a list of the city council of Lincoln was entered on the verso of the first leaf. From the earliest years of the fourteenth century through the latter years of the fifteenth, the margins of the book were in active use as the repository for Lincoln city records. Indeed, casual Lincoln inscriptions can be dated as late as 1610. If the Gospel excerpts added to the beginning of the codex are any indication, the book may very well have been used by city officialdom to take the oaths of office, at least during the fourteenth and fifteenth centuries. Between 1487 and 1559 (but probably early in the sixteenth century), the codex was systematically mutilated by the removal of the upper, outer, and lower parts of all the leaves. Frequently, parts of the Lincoln marginalia were lost and in some instances upper lines of the principal text. The vellum strips were, doubtless, useful in book production but some residual respect for the "oath book" seems to have saved it from total destruction.

After 1610, however, the book seems to have been totally neglected until it was noticed by William Pownall in 1724. Pownall suggested that the Corporation give him the now apparently useless homilies and the Blickling Psalter (MS 10). On 24 March the Corporation duly handed over the books, but Pownall's feigned antiquarian interest was short lived. Very shortly after, he attempted to sell the books to Humfrey Wanley, the librarian for Lord Edward Harley, second Earl of Oxford. But Pownall was dealing simultaneously with Richard Ellys of Nocton, Lincolnshire, and Ellys ultimately bought the volumes for himself. Sometime after 1734, Ellys secured the services of the eminent scholar Michael Maittaire to examine his books. Maittaire evidently studied the homilies closely, for he numbered almost three-fourths of the pages and numbered them correctly, even though they were not bound in the right order.

When Sir Richard Ellys (he had inherited his father's baronetcy in 1727) died in 1742, his library was left to Lady Ellys for her lifetime but seems to have been moved from his London home almost immediately to Blickling Hall in Norfolk. Blickling was the seat of Ellys's ultimate heir, John Hobart, Baron Hobart of Blickling, and already had a famous library. Ellys's books were destined to rest here for nearly two hundred years. The precise ownership of the books is not always clear in the subsequent history of the Hobart family. After a series of complex wills and disclaimers, John Hobart's son and principal heir died without male issue and the son's second daughter (in spite of a variety of claims) came to occupy Blickling with her husband, the second Baron Suffield. Lady Suffield maintained a qualified librarian and made her treasures available to scholars. Dibdin came and in 1843 Benjamin Thorpe came to Blickling and studied the homilies. Probably shortly after Thorpe's visit, Lady Suffield sent the codex to the London bindery of Charles Lewis to be rebound.

In 1850 the Dowager Lady Suffield died without issue and her will provided that the bulk of her property, including her library, pass to the grandson of her elder sister, William Schomberg Robert Kerr, who had in 1841 succeeded his father as the eighth Marquess of Lothian. Scholars continued to come to Blickling and the homilies were noted by the cataloguers of the Historical Manuscripts Commission. In the seventies, the Reverend Mr. Richard Morris did the work for his edition which was published by the Early English Text Society. And then, in the early years of the twentieth century, representatives of the New Palaeographical Society made two facsimile reproductions to illustrate the two major hands of the codex.

In 1930 Philip Henry Kerr succeeded his cousin as the eleventh Marquess and, in order to pay death duties in a period of great economic depression, decided to sell 35 manuscripts and 133 books from his vast library at Blickling at the American Art Association – Anderson Galleries, Inc., in New York. The manuscripts were carefully described in the auction catalogue by Seymour deRicci; lot 2 was the homiliary and it was sold on 27 January 1932 for $55,000 to the dealer Barnet J. Beyer. But the sale was rigged and when the news leaked, the owner of the auction house, Cortlandt Field Bishop, shocked at the bad practices, bought the homilies for his own collection. Bishop lived only three more years, however, and when his collection was put to auction on 5 April 1938, the homilies (lot 285) were bought by Mr. John Hinsdale Scheide of Titusville, Pennsylvania.

Although Titusville was somewhat off the beaten track for scholars, the homiliary still received attention. J. W. F. Hill used the marginalia as a primary source for *Medieval Lincoln*. N. R. Ker managed a full description for his *Catalogue*, albeit based on facsimiles. In 1952, Rudolph Willard arranged with Mr. William H. Scheide (who had inherited his father's library in 1942) to have the homiliary brought to The Pierpont Morgan Library for the preparation of a full facsimile edition. From May 1955 until February 1957 the codex was in New York. The Lewis binding was removed; each leaf was photographed and studied and the leaves were placed in the correct order (for the first time in centuries) and renumbered. The homiliary was rebound by Marguerite Duprez-Lahey and returned to Titusville. In May 1959 Mr. Scheide moved his library to Princeton, New Jersey, where it is now located in a specially built addition to the Princeton University Library.

DeRicci *Census* II, p. 2323, no. 55; Ker 382; DeRicci *Supplement*, p. 314, no. 66.

9

The Will of Æþelgifu

The Scheide Library, Princeton University, Princeton, New Jersey
One leaf; late Xc.

DESCRIPTION

This document is exceptionally large, varying in length from 555 to 567 mm.
and varying in width from 352 to 356 mm.; it survives in excellent condition,
showing only one stain from damp and several inkblots. The sheet was folded
eight times across its width and the nine horizontal sections were then folded
in thirds across; thus, some twenty-seven rectangular sections can be seen
when the leaf is unfolded. A few small holes can be noted in the corners of
these sections. Professor Dorothy Whitelock has observed that this is the largest of all surviving Anglo-Saxon wills and she dates it between 985 and 1002,
"probably not long before 990."

TEXT

It has long been known that Æþelgifu made a will, for a Latin abstract (of
around 300 words) of her instructions was a part of the St. Albans cartulary
which was published as early as 1840, but most notably by W. Birch in volume two of his edition of *Cartularium Saxonicum* in 1887. The actual Old English will is, in contrast, a very substantial document indeed.

Æþelgifu, a well-to-do widow, disposes of fourteen separate estates, three in
Northamptonshire, six in Hertfordshire, and five in Bedfordshire, a good bit
of livestock, a number of slaves, and a good deal of personal property: silver
cups, dishes, horns, wall-hangings, seat covers, bedsteads, chests, a book, a
brooch, saddle-gear, a carriage, as well as her own clothing, singling out
headdresses and kirtles. Even though her major heirs—Ælfnoþ, Ælfwold, and
Leofsige—seem not to have been related to Æþelgifu, she did remember some
of her relatives: her sister's daughter Ælfgifu, her kinswomen Leofrun and
Wulfwynn, and Leofrun's daughter Godwif, her sister's son Leofwine, her sister's son Wulfmær, and his son Leofwine, and her stepdaughter Ælfgifu. She

58

remembered her godson Æþelric with a slave and left specific direct legacies to fourteen other individuals and ten religious institutions. She granted freedom to at least 74 slaves, including Edwin the priest.

Many of the legacies to individuals were only for life or only if the legatee produced children; reversion was almost always in favor of a religious foundation. By far the largest direct bequest, and one generously supplemented by reversionary rights, was to St. Albans, the monastic group which would, thus, have been all-too-well advised to keep track of Æþelgifu's Will. She did not forget the King and "his lady," leaving him, before making any other bequests, thirty mancuses of gold, two stallions, and her deer-hounds. The King's lady was to have thirty additional gold mancuses. These royal legacies, known as *heriot*, constituted a modest precursor of present-day inheritance taxes. But Æþelgifu was far more concerned with her legacies to the spiritual powers than with her benefactions to the King. Many bequests were made with specific personal religious concern. Some gifts to St. Albans were arranged so the monks would provide for her burial, others for the health of her soul and that of her late husband. Gifts to her priests insured vigils and masses and hope for salvation; manumission of slaves was sometimes on condition that devotions be raised on her behalf.

PROVENANCE

Æþelgifu's will was, in all probability, filed with the records of St. Albans, the principal instutional heir of her property. In the seventeenth century it became a part of the muniments of Matthew Hale (1609–1676) who possibly had acquired it from the Saxonist John Selden, whom he served as principal executor. In 1939 Mr. James Fairhurst found this will at Alderley, Matthew Hale's birthplace, and purchased the manuscript, along with other material, from the then owner, Mr. T. E. Sheldon-Hale. Mr. Fairhurst entered negotiations in 1948 to sell his collections. The transactions were to be financed by Messrs. Morgan Grenfell & Co., Ltd. Lord Rennell was a partner of Morgan Grenfell and arranged that when the bulk of the Fairhurst Collection was sold in 1963, the Will would be held back to allow him "to have it studied and published as [his] contribution to the publications of the Roxburghe Club," *The Will of Æthelgifu*, (Oxford, 1968). Then, on 10 December 1969, the Will was sold at Sotheby's as the property of Morgan Grenfell & Co. It was purchased by H. P. Kraus for The Scheide Library.

 **10**

Glosses to the Blickling Psalter

M. 776, The Pierpont Morgan Library, New York, New York
iii+88+i leaves; VIIIc.; glosses, ca. 800 and Xc.; prefatory and closing, XVc.

DESCRIPTION

One of the two great Anglo-Saxon codices in America, these 88 fols. of the original codex, now numbered 1–88 (although fol. 64 is a remnant of the lost beginning of the original book), have been modestly trimmed from their original size. They now measure between 302 and 305 mm. vertically and between 225 and 230 mm. across. The rulings are for twenty-four lines and seem to be made from either the hair or flesh side. Prickings survive in both margins as well as single bounding lines on each side, forming a grid which is 231 by 157 mm. The leaves are gathered in eight, but occasionally in ten. The remnant of the principal codex can be collated as follows: 1^{4-2}, $2–4^{8-1}$, $5–7^8$, 8^{8-4}, 9^{10}, 10^{-1+1}, 11^8, 12^{8+1}. Gatherings 1–2, 6–8, and 11 are laid with all flesh sides out; gatherings 3, 5, 9, and 12, with almost all flesh sides out; gathering 4 alternates each leaf in laying out the quire; gathering 10 has more hair sides out than flesh sides but no regular pattern of alternation is established.

E. A. Lowe has dated the principal script, a splendid Anglo-Saxon majuscule, from the eighth century. Many initials are lavishly ornamented and the interlace design is common; there are also birds, monsters, as well as human faces in a variety of positions. A few glosses to the Psalms were added in red ink in a rounded minuscule hand of the late eighth or early ninth century; other and many more glosses to the Psalter text were added in black ink in a square minuscule hand of the tenth century. A fifteenth-century calendar has been added at the beginning of the volume and a fifteenth-century leaf with quotations from each Gospel has been added at the end.

The blind-tooled goatskin binding is modern and was done by M. Duprez-Lahey.

This impressive codex contains a substantial part of a Latin Psalter of the Roman use, preserving Psalms 31:3–50:19, 52:7–94:6, 101:10–108:31, 111:5–end of Psalm 150, with only a few omissions. Verses 9–30 of Psalm 9 are inserted on a separate fol. 64 amidst the text of the Psalm numbered 116. Twenty-one glosses were added in red ink in the late eighth or early ninth century. Over seven hundred more were added in black ink in the tenth; eleven of these latter glosses provide Latin synonyms in addition to the principal Old English gloss; two are longish marginal notations. There are a number of marginal jottings from the sixteenth and seventeenth centuries, added both to the fifteenth-century calendar and to the Psalter itself.

PROVENANCE

The peregrinations of this Psalter from its origins at the high period of Anglo-Saxon manuscript production are strongly parallel to the Blickling Homilies, MS 8 in this catalogue. E. A. Lowe has identified the script and decoration in the Psalter as the Canterbury style of the eighth century. From these origins, however, the exact whereabouts of the manuscript are not known until the early years of the sixteenth century. Then it most surely was the property of the Lincoln Corporation, for a number of Lincoln officials have graced these pages with their autographs between 1505 and 1635; in addition, the feast for the translation of St. Hugh of Lincoln has been added to the Calendar. In 1724 William Pownall persuaded the Lincoln Corporation to give him the Psalter. He was an enterprising man, and lost no time in trying to sell it for a profit to antiquaries. He offered it to Humfrey Wanley but the sale ultimately went to Richard Ellys, a Member of Parliament and a thoughtful collector. Richard Ellys studied the manuscript carefully and secured attention for it from the scholar Michael Maittaire, who showed it to "Dr. Bentley, Dr. Walker, and Mr. Casley" and verified his suspicion that this manuscript was "as old as anything" they had "in Latin." At Ellys's death in 1742, his library passed to his relatives, the Hobart family of Blickling Hall. The Psalter was carefully preserved there and made available to E. Brock in the early eighteen-seventies for the preparation of his edition of the glosses, to Henry Sweet in the eighteen-eighties when he prepared his edition of the earliest words, and later to the officials of The New Palaeographical Socitey for the production of facsimiles. In 1932, the Marquess of Lothian, who had succeeded to Blickling

Hall and its library, offered a number of his books for sale. The Psalter was sold as lot 1 in the American Art Association sale on 27 January; it was acquired by Dr. A. S. W. Rosenbach and later sold to The Pierpont Morgan Library.

DeRicci *Census* II, p. 1502; Ker 287; *Codices Latini Antiquiores*, no. 1661; part XI, pp. 24-25 and 36, facsimile of part of fol. 40r.

ÆElfric, trans., Bible, O.T., *Heptateuch, Exodus*

G. 63, William S. Glazier Collection, The Pierpont Morgan Library,
New York, New York
Fragments: four leaves; XIc.

DESCRIPTION

These four leaves are all that is now known to remain of a much larger mid-eleventh-century manuscript of ÆElfric's translation of the Heptateuch. Leaves 1 and 4 are conjugate, as are 2 and 3, but while 1 and 3 are virtually complete (measuring 280 by 187 mm.), 2 and 4 are little more than generous stubs (measuring 280 by 53 mm. and 280 by 62 mm., respectively). Thus, each conjugate pair has one full leaf and one fragmentary leaf. Both conjugate pairs were ruled from the hair side of the vellum and were placed in the gathering with hair side out. No prickings survive, but each leaf is ruled for twenty-five lines of text with two bounding lines on each side. The grid is 202 by 166 mm. (including both sets of bounding lines). A comparison of the preserved text with the full biblical narrative shows that these conjugate pairs were the first and third conjugates in a four-conjugate (i.e., eight-leaf) quire. Thus, these fragments preserve all of leaf 1 (r and v), parts of leaf 3 (r and v), all of leaf 6 (r and v), and parts of leaf 8 (r and v) in the original gathering.

The rationale for the curiously analogous mutilation of these two rather clean sheets becomes clear when the patterns of stain and offset are examined. Fol. 1 verso shows a lighter section along the spine edge which follows the outline of the fragmentary fol. 4; the bluish capital *D* on fol. 4 recto is offset on fol. 1 verso (and even through to fol. 1 recto). These facts indicate that fols. 1 and 4 were pressed together for a long time after the manuscript was mutilated. The same characteristics are visible on fols. 2 and 3; fol. 3 recto shows a lighter portion along the left side which follows the outlines of the stub fol. 2; fols. 2 and 3 are also heavily and similarly wrinkled and similarly stained near the spine edge. On both fol. 1 and fol. 3 one can see the outlines of the end of a piece of binding leather as it would appear if secured around to the inside of a binding board; these outlines indicate that these full original leaves were pressed against the inside of binding boards, probably as flyleaves. The original conjugate folds were secured at the spine of the book with the stub nearer the board, but probably neither was pasted down; otherwise, they would now be much dirtier. Thus, the darkened parts of each leaf were next to the board; the cleanest parts where stub faced whole leaf; more normal wear on the side facing the book. The direction of the impressions formed by the leather fold-over indicates that fols. 1 and 4 were used at the end of the book; fols. 2 and 3, at the front. The hand is a clear insular minuscule with a distinctive flourish at the end of the cross mark on ð, at the end of abbreviation marks, and at the lower terminus of "yogh." Pointing is at the line. Ker calls the script "unusual and not good" and dates it "probably . . . in the second half of the eleventh century." Five small initials are preserved on these fragments, *H* in *He* at fol. 3v3; *M* in *Moyses* at fol. 3v5 and 10; *S* in *Syþþan* at fol. 3v21; *D* in *Drihten* at fol. 4r20. The first three were decorated within the regularly formed letters; the latter two were specially made, the last filling the space of two lines of text.

These manuscript leaves are bound in dark blue morocco.

TEXT

The text of fol. 1 begins with Exodus 16:16 and goes through 17:14; this version is closely related to Ælfric's text as it was published from the more complete manuscripts: British Library MS Cotton Claudius B IV (Ker 142), as collated with Bodleian MS Laud Misc. 509 (Ker 344) and other manuscripts. This fragmentary manuscript starts near the beginning of the story about the manna distributed by God to the Israelites in the Sinai desert (Exodus 16:16) and continues without interruption through the miraculous gift of water from the rock and the victory over Amalek (Exodus 17:14). Fol. 2 preserves only small parts of Exodus 19:6 through 20:21; this passage covers Moses's initial hesitation in going up Mt. Sinai, his eventual journey, and the granting of the Ten Commandments. The third leaf again preserves Ælfric's text from Exodus 23:8 through 29:12 (the Old English Heptateuch had no chapters 25–28), an elaborate sequence of law. The last fragmentary leaf preserves only small parts of Exodus 29:46 through 32:24 (the Old English Heptateuch had no chapter 30 and only verses 12–18 of chapter 31), another series of laws, including the account of Moses's breaking the stone tablets in his rage at the worship of the golden calf.

Above the text on fol. 3 verso is written in ink: "Bx 221. N fo 1863". At first, 1863 was written 1663 but the first 6 was corrected to 8 and then the whole number was crossed out and rewritten. A capital letter was also written above the corrected 8 and then crossed out; all these corrections were done by the same hand which made the informal inscription. In the lower margin of that same page is a pencil inscription: "L.1.11." Since fol. 3 verso was once the front flyleaf of a book, perhaps these inscriptions indicate pressmarks. There is also an erasure below the text on fol. 3 verso but an Arabic 3 survives clearly below what probably was a signature with at least three descenders in it, one a large loop. On fol. 1, once the rear flyleaf in the bookbinding, the figures "2 – 6" are written in ink in the middle of the upper margin and "2:6" is written in the upper right corner, also in ink. The pencil notation strikes me as of the nineteenth century. The ink inscriptions are earlier, possibly even from the later seventeenth century.

Nothing is known about the destruction of the original codex of which these leaves were a part, nor about the leather-bound book in which they were used as endpapers. After these leaves were removed from the book they were elaborately bound in dark blue morocco by Sangorski and Sutcliffe in London for Bernard Quaritch, Ltd., but incorrectly identified as twelfth-century on a title page and the spine. This binding probably was done after 1922, the first publication of Crawford's text of the *Old English Heptateuch*, because the text is identified in accord with the peculiarities of the *Heptateuch* chapters and verses. Some time later the stamped gold words on the inside front cover, "For Bernard Quaritch, Ltd.," were carefully covered by a tiny thin strip of matching morocco. Ker reports (in his account of these leaves in his additions to the 1969 reissue of Crawford) that "the leaves were found by Messrs. Quaritch lying loose inside an eighteenth-century printed book" and that Quaritch sold them to H. P. Kraus in New York. Kraus offered them for sale in 1961 in his Catalogue 95, *Twenty-five Manuscripts*, and they were purchased by Mr. William Simon Glazier of New York, but shortly after Mr. Glazier's sudden death in 1962 they were moved to The Pierpont Morgan Library by the Trustees of the Glazier Collection. When the Trust is terminated, Mr. Glazier's collection will become the property of the Morgan Library. The tiny added strip of morocco was removed on 21 August 1975.

1. Constitutional Treatise on the Kingdom of the Franks

Library of Coella Lindsay Ricketts, Chicago, Illinois
Fragment: one leaf

2. Saint's Life

Library of Coella Lindsay Ricketts, Chicago, Illinois
Fragment: one leaf

Seymour deRicci, in his *Census of Medieval and Renaissance Manuscripts*, describes the important collection of Mr. C. L. Ricketts, then located in the First National Bank Building of Chicago. Mr. Ricketts was a calligrapher himself and his collection included examples of many styles of writing and illumination. The individual leaves are not all separately described, but deRicci does note (1, 660) that

Mr. Ricketts also purchased from Tregaskis (Cat. 720, 1912, n. 36 = 706, 1911, n. 17) a series of early fragments described as follows in the vendor's catalogue: "Anglo-Saxon MSS. Fragments of two 9th century MSS. on vellum, one being a portion of a constitutional treatise, apparently on the kingdom of the Franks, the other a portion of the life of a saint, mounted in book, folio, with 24 other fragments, including four pages of a fine fourteenth-century manuscript of Ortolis van Baierland's Arzneibuch in old German, portions of the works of Sidonius Apollinaris, Mathias Farinator, Vincent of Beauvais, etc., boards. — The Anglo-Saxon fragments contain 34 lines on two folio half leaves, both sides being intact and in good state."

He further obtained several single leaves from Tregaskis, Cat. 764 (1 Dec. 1914)....

Several calligraphic manuscripts were purchased from the Ricketts collection by the Newberry Library in 1941 but the Anglo-Saxon leaves were not among them (DeRicci *Supplement*, pp. 146, 156, 157, 159). Two items from the Ricketts collection were presented to Yale University by Mr. and Mrs. David Wagstaff in 1943, but neither was Anglo-Saxon (DeRicci *Supplement*, p. 35). In

1961, the bulk of the C. L. Ricketts collection was acquired by The Lilly Library of Indiana University, but again the Anglo-Saxon fragments were not to be found. Neither Mr. Jasper S. King, Mr. Ricketts's son-in-law and successor in their modern calligraphic work, nor Mr. Ricketts's daughters knew what had become of these two important leaves. Since their destruction cannot be attested, one can yet hope that they will be found.

PLATES

MS Ia

PLATE I

MS 1b

PLATE 2

MS 2

PLATE 3

MS 4

MSS 3a and b

PLATE 4

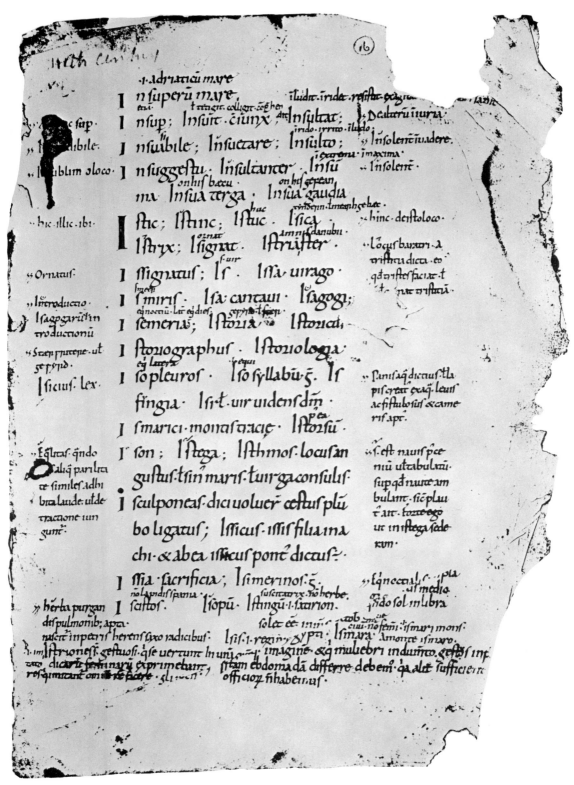

MS 5

PLATE 5

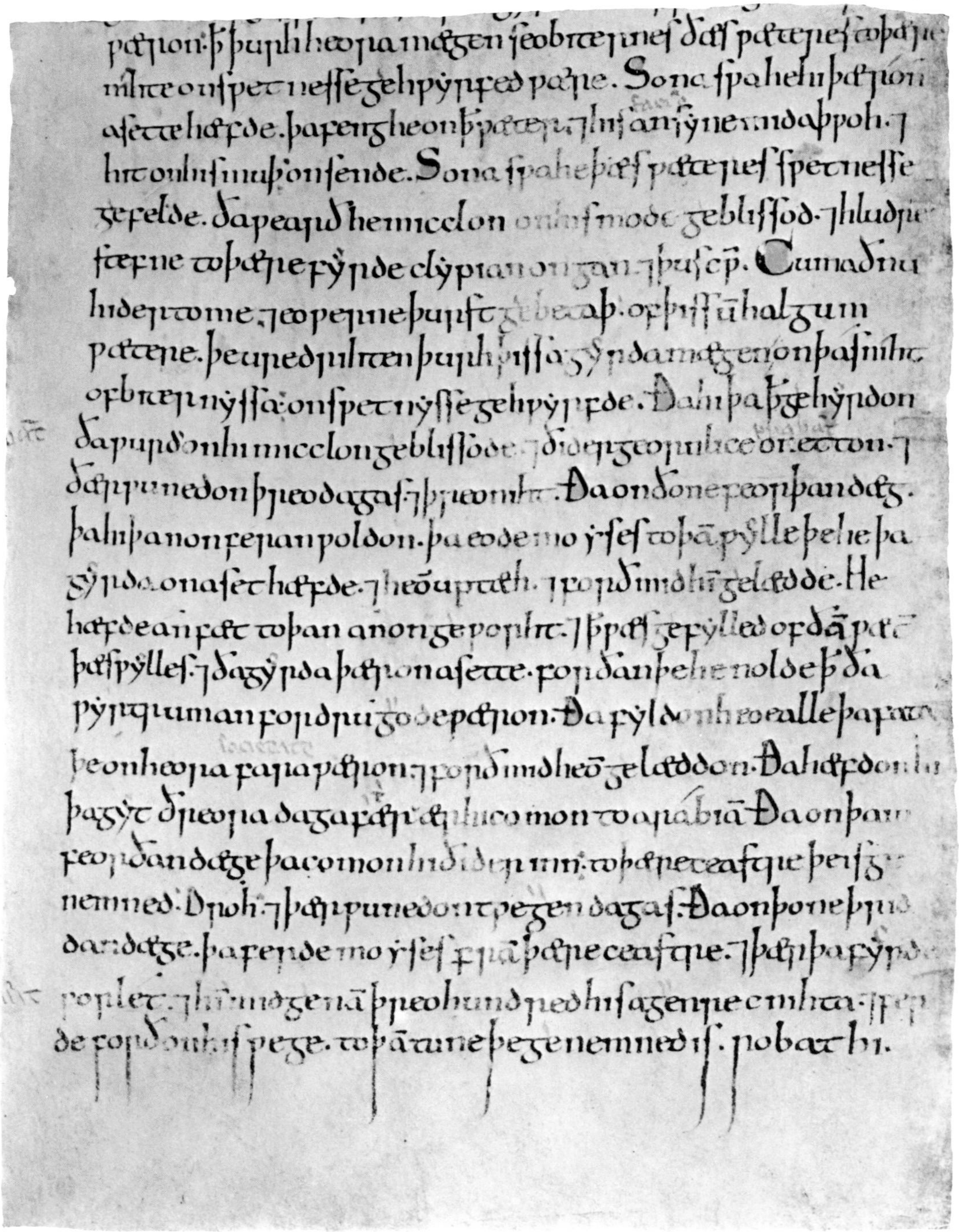

PLATE 6

cpæð þycnyscon hpænne he cuman polde· forþan
ðe þe nycon conanui ǥpiſſe þænne repelpilleroa
ciuſt uſpyle habbancobim ·ofþyrreiu yſinðe
cocecere myſiðe· Ihpæt penſe þula· hpaiſ ǥeqico
þa þeoþa ꝛſhocociꞃ þone þeſe hlaſoꝛo ſecce oſeꞃ
hiꞃ hiꞃeðe· þehiꝺo heoꞃamecæ onꝛihc ne cman
Ælcum hlaſoꝛoe ǥoaꝼenað þhecðhiꞃ mannu
ſymble heoꞃa biᵹ leoꝼan onǥeſecuccoman · ac
ꞃehalenomcenoe þone ǥaſclican mecæ þahalᵹan
lajie· þeᵹmen behoꝛiað coꞃꞃui ſaꝛlui cobyᵹleo
ꝼan þaᵹ ſceolon ǥinyþan æccoꝛꞃui laꞃcoꝛum·
ꞃþa ꞃꝛahi leojiuiað onbocu· Seᵹe cꞃeoꝛaꝛeoꞃa
ꞃꝛe ſnoceꞃiaiꞃꝛe coꝛalaꞃcoꝛ onᵹꝛoeꞃ ǥelaþunᵹe·
þeſeᵹð þahalᵹanlaꞃie· þam læꝛeðu ꝼolce· ꞃꝛaꞃꝛa
þeꞃ halᵹaþꝗuiɫɫoꝛꝺe þepe pujioiað coꝺaꞃ· he
oæloe pjꞃlice onǥþjꞃꞃucman þone ǥaſclican
mecæ ǥoðeꞃ hiꞃeðe ſymie· Ihemaneᵹa ſaꝛlamco
hiꞃ laꞃie ǥeꝼꞃꞃynoe þamælmihciᵹan ǥoðe þehine
nyꝛuꞃioiað· Ðahalᵹan aꝛcaꞃ þeſam hælenoe ꝼol
ᵹoꝺon ꝛaꞃuon þaᵹ cꞃeoꞃan þeoꝛan ꞃþaꝛyꞃimeꞃ
caꞃ byꝺelaꞃ· þeᵹoꝺeꞃ laꞃie ᵹeono þaꞃlano coſeo
pon· ꞃꝛaþheoꝛaboꝺuᵹe ſꝛeᵹ· ſꝛeᵹoe ᵹeono eall·
Iheoꞃapoꝛo becomonco eoꞃþan ǥmꞃꞃuꞃ· Eacheoꞃa
aꝛꝛeꞃꞃeꞃᵹon· Iþa æþelan conꝼeꞃꝛoꞃieꞃ cyðoon
ᵹoꝺeꞃ laꞃie· oꝺꝺæc hic comcꞃuꝛ· Nuſceoleþe eac
ſecᵹan þaſoꝛan laꞃie coꞃ nyꝛonuꞃꞃuꞃ ucman· elleꞃ

MS 7

PLATE 7

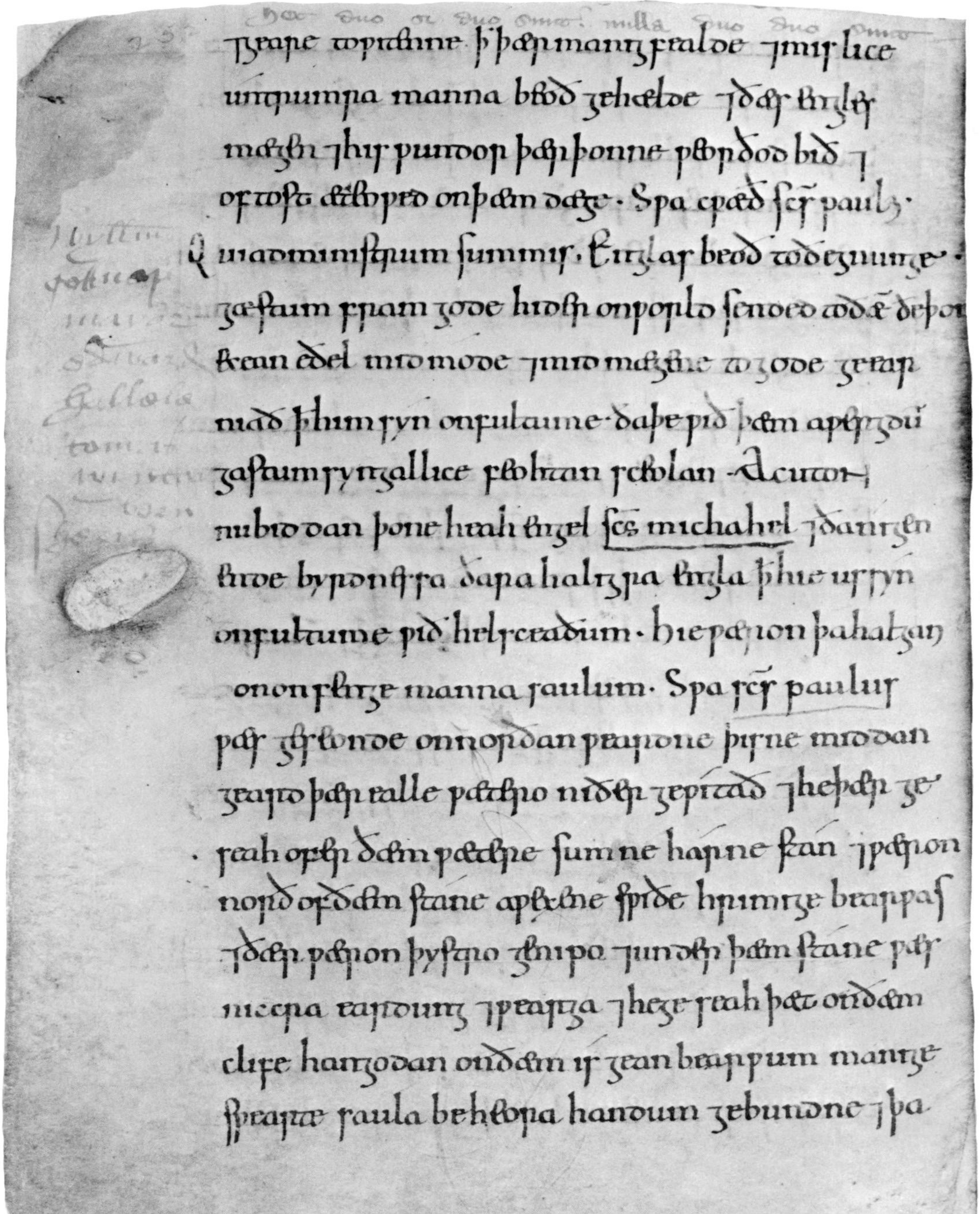

ꞅꝩꞃaꝼe copꞃaꞇꞇne þ̄ þ� mann ꝼꞃalꝺe ꞇꝼmꞇ lice
untꞃꝩmꞇa manna bꝛoꝺ ꞡehælꝺe ꝼꝺaꞅ Eꞃꞡꞅ
mæꞡn ꝼhꝩꞅ ꝼunꝺoꝛ þaꞃ þonne ꝼꝵꝛ ꝺoꝺ bꝩꝺ ꞇ
oꝼ ꞇoꞅꞇ æꞇꝵꝼꞃeꝺ onþæm ꝺæꞡe · Spa cpæꝺ ꝼcꞅ paulꝵ ·
Qui aꝺmmꝛꞇꝛaꞇum ꞅummꝛꞅ · Eꞃꞡꝛaꞅ bꝛoꝺ coꝺeꞡꝩnꞃꞡe ·
ꞡæꞅꞇum ꝼꝛam ꞡoꝺe hꞃoꝼꞅ onꝼopꞇo ꞅcꞃoꝺe coꝺæ ꝺꞃꝵꞃ
ꝵꞃean æꝺel mꞃꝺ moꝺe ꞇꞃmꞇo mæꞃꞡꝛe co ꞡoꝺe ꞡꞃꞃap
mæꝺ þꝵꞃmꞅꝩn onꝼulaꝛme · ꝺaþe pꞃꝺ þæm aꝵꞃꞡꝛoꝵ
ꞡaꞅꞇum ꝩꞃꞡallꝛce ꝼꝵꞃaꞇan ꞃꝵꞃꝺlan · Acuꞇoꞃꞅ
nꝵbꝛoꝺan þone hꞃah Eꞃꞡꝵ ꞅcꞅ michahꝵl ꞇꝺaꞃꞃꞡꝵn
ꞇꝼꝵꝺe bꝩꞃonꞅꞇꞃa ꝺaꝼa halꞃꞡꞃa Eꞃꞡla þꝵ̄hꝵ ꝵꞃꝼꝩn
onꝼulaꞃme pꝛꝺ hꞃꝼꞃccaꝺꝵm · hꞃeꝵ̄ꞃon þahaꞇꞡꝵn
onon ꝼꞃꞃꞡe manna ꞅaꝵlꝵm · Spa ꝼcꞃ paulꝵꞅ
þaꞅ ꞡꞅꝼꝵꝛꝺe onnoꞃꝺan ꝵꞃaꞃꝺne þꞃꞃne mꞃꝺ ꝺan
ꞡꞃaꞃꝺ þæꞃ ꞃalle þæꞃꞃꝛo nꞃꝺꝵꞃ ꞡeꝵꞃcæꝺ ꞇheþæꞃ ꞡe
ꞃꝵah oꝵꞃꞃ ꝺæm þælꞃꞃꝼe ꞅꝵmne hꞃꞃꞃne ꞅꝵan ꞇꝵꝵꞃꞃon
noꞃꝺ oꝼꝺæm ꞅꞃane apꝛꞃꞃꝺe ꞅ̄ꝩꝛꝺe hꞃꝵꞃꞃꞡe bꞃꝵꝼꝵaꞅ
ꞇꝺæꞃꞃ þꞃꞃꝛon þꝩꞅꝵꞃo ꞡꞃꝵꞃꝺa ꞇꝵꞃꝺꞃꞃ þæꝛ ꞅꞃane þæꞅ
mꞃꞃꝛa ꞃaꞅoꝵꞃꞡ ꞇꞃꞃaꞃꞡa ꞇheꞡe ꞃꝵah þæꞅ oꞃꝺæm
clꝛꝼe haꞃꞡoꝺan oꝵꝺæm ꞃꞅ ꞡean bꞃꝵꝼꝵum mannꞃꞡe
ꞅꞃꞃaꞃꞃꝺe ꞃaꝵla behꞃꝵꞃa hanꝺꝵm ꞡebꝵꞃꝺonꞃ ꞇꝼa

MS 8, fol. 126v

PLATE 8

TO SCA MARTINES MÆSSAN

127

PLATE 9

MS 9

PLATE 10

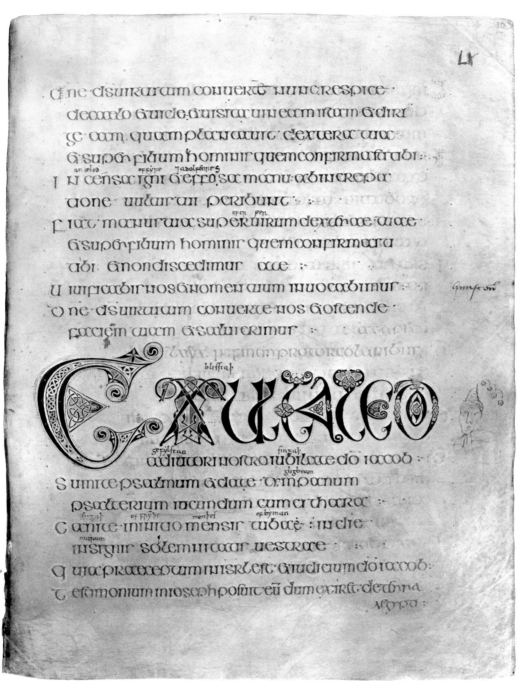

MS 10

PLATE II

fæt ful. þe hi gomor heton. ⁊ þa beapn dydon spa ⁊ ga-
dpodon. sum mape sum læsse. Se ðe mape gadepode næfde
na mape ne se þe læsse gadepode næppe na læsse. ac ælc þ
ge noh hæfde. Ða bead moyses heom þ hi hit nan þing ne
læfdon oþen niht. þa læfdon hi hit sume oð hit mopgen
pæs. ⁊ hit pearð pyrmum cpeopyð ⁊ hit for potode. þa pæs
moyses ypppe ⁊ hi gadepodon on mopgen þ hi ge hæfdon.
⁊ þa seo sunne pearm þa for meolt hit. On þã syxtan dæge
hi ge gadepodon tpy fealdlice. þa comon þa ealdpas ⁊ þehton
hit moyse. þa cp he to hii fæðrnes dæges pest is dpihtne
ge halgod gpap piað to mepigen þ ge to gap pienne habbon.
⁊ hatldað oþ mepigen þ þap to lafe beo. þa dydon hi spa. ⁊
hit ne potode ne lune fundon nan þinge fules þæp on
And moyses cp eað hit to dæg fon þan þe hit dpihtnes pir
ten dæg. fon þam ge hit ne findaþ to dæg on eorþan. gade
piað hit .vi. dagas ne finde ge hit on þã seofoðan. hi eodon
ut on þã seofoðon dæge ⁊ ne fundon nan þinge. þa cp
dpihten to moyse hu lange nelle ge healdan mine beboda.
on þã syxtan dæge he hii sylð tpi fealdne mete. beo ælc æt
hã ⁊ ne ga nan ut on þam seofoðan dæge ⁊ peste þ folc
hit on þã seofoðan dæge ⁊ nemdon þoii mete man. þæs
spæc pæs spylce smedma mid hunige ⁊ moyses het ni
man þ ge met fæt ful. ⁊ settan he foran dpi htne on
þã ge telde to healdene. Israhela beapn æton heoponliene
mete feopentig pintpa oþ hi comon to chanaan lande.

PLATE 12

BIBLIOGRAPHY

Ælfric. *Grammatik und Glossar*. Edited by Julius Zupitza. Berlin: Weidmann-sche Buchhandlung, 1880.

Ælfric. *The Homilies of the Anglo-Saxon Church . . . the Sermones Catholici, or Homilies of Ælfric*. Edited by Benjamin Thorpe. Two volumes. London: The Ælfric Society, 1844–46.

Ælfric. *Lives of Saints*. Edited by Walter W. Skeat. Early English Text Society, o.s. 76, 82, 94, 114. London: N. Trübner & Co., 1881–1900.

Bibliotheca Phillippica. New Series: Medieval Manuscripts, Part V. . . . London: Sotheby & Co., 1969.

Birch, Walter deGray, ed. *Cartularium Saxonicum*. Three volumes. London: Whiting and Co., 1885–93.

Birlinger, A. "Bruchstück aus Alfric's Angelsächsischer Grammatik," *Germania* 15 (1870), 359.

Bond, W. H., and C. U. Faye, eds. *Supplement to the Census of Medieval and Renaissance Manuscripts in the United States and Canada*. New York: The Bibliographical Society of America, 1962.

Bosworth, Joseph N., and T. Northcote Toller. *An Anglo-Saxon Dictionary*. Oxford: Clarendon Press, 1898.

Boyd, Julian. *The Scheide Library*. Princeton, N. J.: privately printed, 1947.

Brock, E. "The Blickling Glosses," in *The Blickling Homilies*, edited by Richard Morris. Early English Text Society, o.s. 63. London: N. Trübner & Co., 1867. Pp. 251–63; reprinted, 1967.

Bryan, Mina R. "Portrait of a Bibliophile: XVII: The Scheide Library," *The Book Collector* 21 (Winter, 1972), 489–502.

Campbell, Alistair. *An Anglo-Saxon Dictionary. Enlarged Addenda and Corrigenda to the Supplement*. Oxford: Clarendon Press, 1972.

Catalogue of the Celebrated Library of the Late Major J. R. Abbey: The Ninth Portion: The Hornby Manuscripts, Part II: Thirty-four Manuscripts of the 9th to the 16th Century. London: Sotheby & Co., 1975.

Catalogue of the Extraordinary Collection of Splendid Manuscripts . . . formed by M. Guglielmo Libri . . . Which Will Be Sold by Auction . . . On Monday, 28th of March, 1859, and Seven following Days. London: J. Davy and Sons, 1859.

Clemoes, Peter. "The Chronology of Ælfric's Works," in *The Anglo-Saxons: Studies . . . presented to Bruce Dickins*, edited by Peter Clemoes. London: Bowes and Bowes, 1959. Pp. 212–47.

Colgrave, Bertram, and Ann Hyde. "Two Recently Discovered Leaves from Old English Manuscripts," *Speculum* 37 (January 1962), 60–78.

Collins, Rowland L. "A Reexamination of the Old English Glosses in the Blickling Psalter," *Anglia* 81 (1963), 124–28.

——— "An Ælfric Manuscript Fragment," *Times Literary Supplement*, 2 September 1960, p. 561.

——— "Ælfric Manuscript Fragments," *Times Literary Supplement*, 31 March 1961, p. 201.

——— "Two Fragments of Ælfric's *Grammar*: The Kinship of Ker 384 and Ker 242," *Annuale Mediaevale* 5 (1964), 5–12.

——— and Peter Clemoes. "The Common Origin of Ælfric Fragments at New Haven, Oxford, Cambridge, and Bloomington," in *Old English Studies in Honour of John Collins Pope*. Toronto: University of Toronto Press, 1974. Pp. 285–326.

Crawford, S. J., ed. *The Old English Version of the Heptateuch. . . .* Early English Text Society, o.s. 160. London: Oxford University Press, 1922; reprinted with additions by N. R. Ker in 1969.

DeRicci, Seymour, and W. J. Wilson. *Census of Medieval and Renaissance Manuscripts in the United States and Canada.* Three volumes. New York: H. W. Wilson Co., 1935–40.

Dickins, Bruce. "The Making of the Parker Library," *Transactions of the Cambridge Bibliographical Society*, VI, pt. 1 (1972), 19–34.

Gneuss, Helmut. *Lehnbildungen und Lehnbedeutungen im Altenglischen.* Berlin: E. Schmidt, 1955.

Hill, J.W.F. *Medieval Lincoln.* Cambridge: University Press, 1948.

Illuminated Manuscripts, Incunabula, and Americana from the Famous Libraries of the Most Hon. the Marquess of Lothian, C.H., Sold by His Order. New York: American Art Association, Anderson Galleries, Inc., 1932.

Ker, N. R. "Membra Disiecta, Second Series," *British Museum Quarterly* 14 (1940), 79–86.

————— *Catalogue of Manuscripts Containing Anglo-Saxon*. Oxford: Clarendon Press, 1957.

Liebert, Herman W. "The Beinecke Library: Accessions 1969," *The Yale University Library Gazette* 44 (April 1970), 165–203.

Lowe, E. A. *Codices Latini Antiquiores. A Palaeographical Guide to Latin Manuscripts Prior to the Ninth Century*. Part I: eleven volumes and supplement; Part II: one volume. Oxford: Clarendon Press, 1934–72.

————— "Membra disiecta," *Revue Bénédictine* 39 (1927), 191–92.

Marston, Thomas E. "The Earliest Manuscript of St. Aldhelm's *De Laudibus Virginitatis*," *The Yale University Library Gazette* 44 (April 1970), 204–06.

Meritt, H. D. "Old English Aldhelm Glosses," *Modern Language Notes* 67 (December 1927), 553–54.

————— "Supplement" to John R. Clark Hall's *A Concise Anglo-Saxon Dictionary*. Fourth edition. Cambridge: Cambridge University Press, 1960.

Migne, Jacques Paul, ed. *Patrologiae cursus completus*. Series Latina. 221 volumes. Paris, 1844–64.

Morrell, Minnie C. *A Manual of Old English Biblical Materials*. Knoxville, Tennessee: University of Tennessee Press, 1965.

Morris, Richard, ed. *The Blickling Homilies*. Early English Text Society, o.s. 58, 63, 73. London: N. Trübner & Co. 1874–80; reprinted, 1967.

Napier, Arthur S. *Old English Glosses*. Anecdota Oxoniensia. Oxford: Clarendon Press, 1900.

————— ed. *History of the Holy Rood-tree*. Early English Text Society, o.s. 103. London: Kegan Paul, Trench, Trübner & Co., Ltd., 1894.

The New Palaeographical Society: Facsimiles of Ancient Manuscripts, &c. Edited by E. M. Thompson *et al*. First series, two volumes. London: Oxford University Press, 1903–12. Second series, two volumes. London: Oxford University Press, 1913–30.

Oldham, J. Basil. *English Blind-Stamped Bindings*. Cambridge: Cambridge University Press, 1952.

Oliphant, Robert T. *The Harley Latin–Old English Glossary*. Janua Linguarum, Series Practica xx. The Hague: Mouton & Co., 1966.

Parks, Stephen. *The Osborn Collection 1934–1974: A Catalogue of Manuscripts Exhibited in the Beinecke Rare Book and Manuscript Library, October 1974 – February 1975*. New Haven: Yale University Library [1974].

Plummer, John. *The Glazier Collection of Illuminated Manuscripts*. New York: The Pierpont Morgan Library, 1968.

Sweet, Henry, ed. *The Oldest English Texts*. Early English Text Society, o.s. 83. London: N. Trübner & Co., 1885. Pp. 122–23.

Toller, T. Northcote. *An Anglo-Saxon Dictionary Supplement*. Oxford: Clarendon Press, 1921.

Whitelock, Dorothy, Lord Rennell, and N. R. Ker. *The Will of Æthelgifu*. Oxford: The Roxburghe Club, 1968.

Wildhagen, Karl. "Studien zum Psalterium Romanum in England und seinen Glossierungen," *Festschrift für Lorenz Morsbach: Studien zur Englischen Philologie* 50 (1913), 431–35.

Willard, Rudolph, ed. *The Blickling Homilies*. Early English Manuscripts in Facsimile, vol. 10. Copenhagen: Rosenkilde and Baggar, 1960.

Wolf, Edwin, II (with John Fleming). *Rosenbach; a Biography*. Cleveland: World Publishing Co., 1960.

Zimmermann, Ernest Heinrich. *Vorkarolingische Miniaturen* (with four volumes of plates). Berlin: Deutscher verein für kunstwissenschaft, 1916–18.

Zupitza, Julius. "Kritische Beiträge zu den Blickling Homilies und Blickling Glosses," *Zeitschrift für deutsches Altertum und deutsche Literatur* 26 (1882), 211–24.

This book was set in Monotype Baskerville and printed at
The Stinehour Press.
The plates were printed at The Meriden Gravure Company.
The patterned paper for the cover,
the border on the title page, and the chapter-head ornaments
were all especially drawn for this edition
by Stephen Harvard.